# BETWEEN THE LINES

# BETWEEN THE LINES

A personal history of the British public
telephone and telecommunications service
1870 – 1990

## Robert C. Morris

Post Office Engineering Department and
British Telecommunications plc 1947 – 1990

ISBN 0 9524034 0 4

British Library Cataloguing in Publication Data. A catalogue record for this book is available from the British Library.

Printed and bound in Great Britain.

*To our Grandchildren Joshua, Rebecca and Andrew,
by the end of whose normal life span the early
history covered by this book will be 200 years old.*

# Contents

# Foreword

by

Dr. Alan Rudge, OBE, FRS, FEng, FIEE
Managing Director, Development and Procurement
British Telecommunications plc

The British public telecommunications service, which dates back to the 19th century, has been subject to continuous change, both technical and political. The recording of this unfolding story has been sporadic; there have been "in-house" announcements of each new technical advance as it has happened, and more voluminous, and often partisan, political comment of the day.

Now someone who spent over forty years within the business has written the story of these times. These pages put over the everyday striving for excellence as well as some of the frustrating difficulties over a period when overall service and value for money gradually improved for the growing number of customers.

Bob Morris provides a unique view of the technical and political factors which affected the people pressing on with their job — insight with a personal touch.

What comes after the period covered by this book is already bringing changes just as radical and sweeping as those described here. There is no doubt that the striving for excellence is a tradition that will continue in telecommunications in this country for the foreseeable future.

# THE ELECTRIC AND INTERNATIONAL
# TELEGRAPH COMPANY.

## INCORPORATED 1846.

The Charges for Messages not exceeding Twenty Words in Great Britain and Ireland :—

| | | | | | |
|---|---|---|---|---|---|
| Within a Circuit of | 50 Miles | ............................................. | **1s. 6d.** |
| Do. do. | 100 do. | ............................................. | **2s. 0d.** |
| Do. do. | 150 do. | ............................................. | **3s. 0d.** |
| Beyond a Circuit of 150 | do. | ............................................. | **4s. 0d.** |
| To or from Dublin | | ............................................. | **5s. 0d.** |

No Charge is made for the Names and Addresses of either Sender or Receiver, or for Delivery within half a mile of the Company's Offices. The Company have

## UPWARDS OF 360 STATIONS IN FULL OPERATION,
### The whole of which are in
## Direct Communication with the Continent,
### Viâ the Company's
## LINE TO THE HAGUE AND AMSTERDAM:
By which, under recent arrangements with the Continental Governments,

## GREAT REDUCTIONS
Have been made in the charges, as shewn in the following list of

### CHARGES TO

| | £ | s. | d. | | £ | s. | d. | | £ | s. | d. |
|---|---|---|---|---|---|---|---|---|---|---|---|
| Amsterdam | 0 | 6 | 0 | Copenhagen | 0 | 12 | 0 | Paris | 0 | 11 | 0 |
| Antwerp | 0 | 7 | 0 | Genoa | 0 | 15 | 6 | Riga | 1 | 5 | 6 |
| Berlin | 0 | 11 | 0 | Hamburg | 0 | 10 | 0 | Rotterdam | 0 | 6 | 0 |
| Bremen | 0 | 8 | 6 | Konigsberg | 0 | 13 | 6 | St. Petersburg | 1 | 11 | 6 |
| Brussels | 0 | 7 | 6 | Malta | 1 | 11 | 0 | Stockholm | 0 | 18 | 0 |
| Christiania | 0 | 18 | 0 | Memel | 0 | 13 | 6 | Trieste | 0 | 12 | 0 |
| Constantinople | 1 | 13 | 6 | Odessa | 1 | 11 | 6 | Vienna | 0 | 12 | 0 |

For information as to number of words allowed, charges to other Stations, &c., &c., apply at any of the Company's Offices.

### PRINCIPAL STATIONS IN GREAT BRITAIN.

| | | | |
|---|---|---|---|
| Aberdeen | Falmouth | London | Sunderland |
| Birmingham | Glasgow | Lowestoft | Swansea |
| Bradford | Gloucester | Manchester | Truro |
| Bristol | Greenock | Newcastle-on-Tyne | Wakefield |
| Cambridge | Halifax | Norwich | Warrington |
| Cardiff | Haverfordwest | Oxford | Whitby |
| Carlisle | Holyhead | Perth | Wolverhampton |
| Darlington | Huddersfield | Plymouth | Windsor |
| Dublin | Hull | Preston | Wigan |
| Edinburgh | Leeds | Sheffield | Yarmouth |
| Exeter | Liverpool | Southampton | York. |

Lothbury, London, June, 1853.                    J. S. FOURDRINIER, Secretary

*Early International communications from the UK, 1853*

10

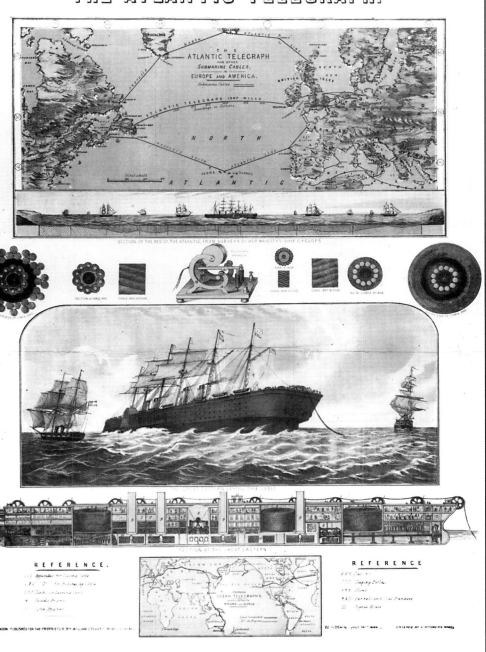

# THE ATLANTIC TELEGRAPH.

*first Transatlantic Cables*

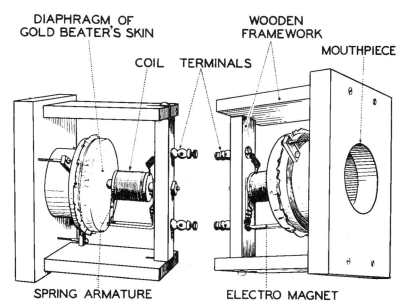

DIAPHRAGM OF
GOLD BEATER'S SKIN

WOODEN
FRAMEWORK

MOUTHPIECE

COIL TERMINALS

SPRING ARMATURE

ELECTRO MAGNET

*Alexander Graham Bell's first Telephone*

*An early Ericsson Telephone*

# Preface

In writing this History of British Telecom and its predecessors I was recommended by Dr G.H. Martin, formerly Professor of History at the University of Leicester and Keeper of the National Archives, to use J.D. Scott's History of Vickers as a model.

Scott returned to management with Vickers after interruption, but I have the advantage of a lifetime of continuous service in British Telecom (BT) and its earlier manifestations, punctuated only by 2 years National Service. I changed jobs, seniority and perspective while the great monolithic Industry itself changed around me, slowly and ponderously at first then, from the late 80s, with near-alarming acceleration with doubtful braking capacity.

Several people have asked me if this is to be an autobiography. In answer I would refer them to the music of Tchaikovsky. The tunes are individual and melodious to many, but beneath every piece is the ever-present theme of the march of Fate, the backdrop which, in my case, is the onward moving Organisation.

Like Scott, I cannot hope to record everything which happened in my 43 years with the Industry, and in the cause of conciseness there is a risk that some items of significance may have been omitted. However, I have attempted to put over the essence of the evolving history of the public telecommunications system in the United Kingdom from the late 19th century to recent times in 1990.

It was my great privilege and advantage to join the Post Office Engineering Department (POED) as an Apprentice in 1947, and to progress in 9 gradual steps, finding myself in late career in charge of a Headquarters section administering contracts for the purchase of BT's £500 million worth of telephone exchange equipment annually. The route between these extremes is akin to a small insect progressing across a multi-coloured patchwork quilt, the patches representing 3 local Area offices, 2 departments in a Regional office, and 5 Headquarters departments, taking responsibility for, carrying out and managing a multitude of Engineering, Clerical and Administrative work types along the way. Throughout I carried out formal management development duties, both within and outside my own units, as an extra-mural activity.

I have great affection for the service to which I have given (or, rather, sold) my working life, so I have tended to regard with disdain the pastime of politicians and other relatively uninformed people to criticise the British public telecommunications service to further, as they imagine, their own ends by discrediting others such as the elected administration.

BT and its predecessors have always had their mainly unseen real problems, and always will have while the Business exists, as in any large company. The main point of variability through history has been their ability to deal with them effectively, depending on which external constraints have been in vogue at the time.

I have not set out to applaud or decry the various constitutional changes which have occurred in the Business, but rather to record them and their effects as seen from the inside, from where I and many others have always attempted to maximise business advantage from successive flavours of the month.

Readers of this book with Engineering exactitude of thought towards the English language may challenge my use of "plastic bins" rather than "plastics bins", and "digitisation" rather than "digitalisation", but I stand resolutely against such developments which I consider, as an old Grammar School boy, to have a devaluing effect upon our language.

It is of interest, at least to me, that I have written this preface and the early part of the book on the terrace of a hotel in Doha, Qatar, where at the age of 59 I am still privileged to be carrying out a worthwhile consultancy role for British Telconsult in my so-called retirement.

To those who ask how I can have enough time to write a book in Qatar when on a contracted mission I would reply that not even the Qataris work in the afternoons due to the blazing heat of their desert climate, in which morning work lasts from 7 am to 2 pm, 6 days a week.

RCM

Doha, Qatar

September 1990

# Acknowledgments

I wish to give thanks to the UK telecommunications business, in its successive forms, for putting up with me in its employment for nearly half a century, and to David Savill, the BT Deputy Secretary, for his guidance, encouragement and help in the recording and publication of my experiences; to Colin Browne, former BT Director of Corporate Relations, Simon Evans, BT Group Promotions Manager, and the editorial staffs of the BT house magazines, for their support; to David Hay and Norman Harris of the BT Archives and Historical Information Office; to Neil Johannessen of the BT Museum; and to Justin Quillinan, Herb Snijder and Brian Denyer for their practical help and guidance in publication. My thanks go also to my old school contemporaries at the Colchester Royal Grammar School, the late Dr. Roy Cresswell, and Professor Geoffrey Martin, for their encouragement to me to start writing this book.

I thank also all the real-life characters mentioned in the book, with special thanks to the late Clifford Riley MBE, and to all my other ex-colleagues who remain anonymous.

Above all I thank Marian, my long-suffering wife, for not going completely round the bend during the 3 years I took to write it (including the last 4 chapters composed in flight over the Atlantic en route to Venezuela to celebrate our 30th wedding anniversary).

RCM

Puerto la Cruz

Venezuela

November 1992

*Traditional Post Office Telephone Kiosk*

*An early Pay-on-Answer Coin Box*

*300-Type Telephone with Combined Bell*

# Introduction

Please do not close the book when I suggest that to catch some of the nuances and subtleties which follow, it will help to have a mental image of roughly how a telephone call is made.

The principle is no more technical than switching on a light in one's house. To make the light work a switch must be operated. Choice of the switch determines which light comes on, assuming the bulb or the fuse has not blown. Now imagine you have an obedient servant to operate the switches for you. Tell him which light you wish to glow and he will choose the switch and operate it.

The lights are Telephones and the servant is a robot called the Public Telephone Exchange. In reality the exchange is a wonder of modern technology worth on average about £3 million, which takes its switching instructions from whatever you key into any phone. If you ask it to switch lights on in (ie, make calls to) places outside your own house (ie, outside your local exchange area) our robot servant will instruct (ie, "signal" to) others of his kind elsewhere in the country or the world, sometimes over short linking lines called Junctions, and sometimes long ones called Trunks. Lastly, don't be fooled by the popular concept of a Line, as it could easily be a radio link or an optic fibre carrying light rays, as well as the more familiar electrical impulses over wires.

I now change the scene to the bleak road from Colchester to West Mersea, in Essex, in the snowy December of 1947. The junction lines from the automatic exchange in Colchester to the manual exchange (ie, one with real live servants called Operators) at West Mersea comprised 32 thin copper wires on the 12-mile pole route, but the increase in post-war telephone traffic meant that these wires were now insufficient in number to carry the traffic at peak times. More than 32 wires on the route would overload the poles, and so were not allowed.

So the Post Office Engineering Department (POED) had the job of replacing the wires with a lead-covered cable of higher capacity. Lead sheathed cable is much heavier than copper, so its suspension steel rope had to be tensioned to 4 tonnes to support the cable without sagging, necessitating the strengthening of all the poles on the 12-mile route, and the struts and stays which kept them upright.

I was an Apprentice with the construction gang following on after the route-strengthening party, putting up the steel rope and the cable. Although only a callow youth of 16, I was given a 45-foot telescopic wooden ladder, a safety belt,

*Ladder work in the snow, 1950s*

a boring tool called an auger, and a canvas tool bag known as a bass full of 18-inch bolts. The gang left me alone on the road, totally responsible for putting the suspension steel bolts through the tops of the poles. All day long I plodded slowly towards West Mersea, equipping one pole after another. When I reached The Strood, the causeway on to Mersea Island, the wind was blowing the snow horizontally from the west, and while boring the hole at the top of one pole the wind blew the heavy ladder down into the road. There I waited, like some elevated snowman, until at last a brave lone cyclist, a man advanced in years, struggled to re-erect my escape route. But the job got done, and my sense of achievement was great indeed when supping gang tea ( a vile brew containing a dash of creosote from the wood smoke) at the end of the day before returning to base. A couple of years later new Engineering Instructions making the lashing of the tops of ladders to poles with rope mandatory were issued from Headquarters in London.

The next day I reached the "cross-arm" pole where the road forked to East and West Mersea, and 3 lots of up to 32 wires converged on the pole, leaving me a tiny triangular space in which to wriggle up between them. It was near the end of the day and, try as I may, I could not get down again. My gang foreman, Arthur "Titch" Hamilton would hear none of my protestations, and threatened to return to Colchester without me. So I had no choice, coming down any way I could, drawing a little blood here and there as I did so.

At my retirement ceremony in BT Headquarters over 42 years later in 1990, I recalled the blunt but highly effective management techniques of such men as Titch Hamilton, suggesting that they were, in their way, better managers than some of the latter day captains of industry.

I mentioned Engineering Instructions (EIs) earlier. While party politicians were, even in 1947, maligning in general terms the service which we in the POED strove to achieve, the real problem worthy of criticism went entirely unnoticed externally. EIs were designed to cover absolutely everything done in the name of the POED. Thus, thousands of specialist experts filled such places as 2-12 Gresham Street, Armour House and River Plate House, in London, slowly developing designs and procedures to leave the field staff in no doubt at all as to how to do it. This situation persisted into the latter half of the century and, now under the banner of Telecommunications Instructions (TIs) I found an Engineer in 1978 who had spent 4 years, no less, designing a Teleprinter Trolley, with careful and brilliant concept for making it walk its wheels up and down stairs, only to find that someone else in Headquarters had had the temerity to re-design the Teleprinter.

Another feature of EIs and TIs was the Staff Rules contained therein. These always seemed a bit severe and inflexible to me, but the great challenge was ever to win an argument with the ageing spinsters in the Regional and Headquarters offices who defended their written word with dogged determination if someone from the Field dared to raise a question. I regret rather the passing of these female dragons with the coming of the new-style BT and thus the demise of the TIs. But our gang foremen dismissed all this by training my colleagues and myself to believe that the "EIs are only a guide".

*Working on a Cross-Arm Pole*

Why choose my early days as an Apprentice as introduction to this book ? 1947/48 was very much a pivotal period when Industry at large was giving itself a shake after World War 2, midway between the first involvement of the POED in telephony at the turn of the century and the coming of the privatised BT in the mid-80s. To work in the POED just after World War 2 was considered a great privilege and achievement by those in the service. Life was very solid and ordered, and seemed as if it would go on for ever without change. It represented a wide career plateau. The radical changes which were to come upon us were then a totally closed book, as were the hardships of the pre-War years.

*National Telephone Company (NTC) Overhead Line Plant*

*A Contractor Mole-Ploughing underground telephone cables by horse. Early 20th century*

# Chapter 1

# *The Beginnings*

As I joined the POED in 1947 I can claim only to have referred knowledge of the "old days" back to 1908 and beyond.

When I was accepted into the service, some of my colleagues then about to retire dated back in their careers to around 1908, and thus told me from first hand about the troublesome yet fulfilling working lives they had experienced.

I was also inevitably involved from time to time in the "low work ebb" pursuit of recovering redundant heavy gauge overhead copper wires from pole routes beside the A12 Ipswich to London road which, as in all parts of Britain, were erected by the former National Telephone Company (NTC) up to the year 1896, and thereafter by the POED to the end of the century. As copper prices had inflated out of all recognition and these wires each weighed 1 tonne per 3 miles, such recovery of beds of up to 32 wires was a very lucrative activity indeed for the POED. The NTC's overhead construction excellence was a joy to behold, beautifully provided with great precision and strength on huge "stout" poles as hard as iron after years of seasoning in situ, and often 7 feet in circumference. The transfer of responsibility for the trunk network from the NTC to the POED in 1896 was largely a political decision by the Liberal Government of the day, so representing the first move towards public ownership of the UK telecommunications network.

In the very early days of the Magneto manual exchange (the type on which you "rang off" after the completion of a call by turning a handle), urban customers' telephone lines were suspended straight on to their houses from the tops of monstrous 65-foot stout poles located at the rear of commercial offices and shops, like great unlovely maypoles. The ladder with which I trudged along the Mersea road in 1947 was a late refinement, as most pre-World War 2 pole climbing was achieved by the use of Climbers, inward-pointing spikes at shoe level, strapped to the shins. Their use was not easy, but the technique was soon learned after a couple of lots of splinters in the inner legs on the descent. But the 65-foot stouts in the towns were different, as they were too large in diameter for the use of Climbers, so the pole steps on them were provided right down to ground level, presenting the climber with a vertical (or sometimes near-vertical!) marathon before actually doing work at the top, way above the town.

An old friend of mine, Stanley J. Last, who retired from the Southend-on-Sea

*Fitting Climbers before climbing a Pole. 1930s*

25

*Laying Heavy-Gauge Underground Cable*

◄ *Working on an H-Pole*

Telephone Area around 1955 as an Executive Engineer, told me about the time he started his work life as a Post Office Boy Messenger at the famous old PO building at 7, Museum Street, Ipswich, and took his lunchtime sandwiches to the very top of the 65-foot stout in the yard, without permission. Oddly, in 1956, it fell to my lot as an External Planner to recover this venerable 70-year-old pole, a difficult task since many later buildings had hemmed it in since it was erected. So we got it out by erecting another tall pole as a derrick, and lifted it horizontally over the roof of 7, Museum Street while the police closed the road to traffic. Many others had to be sawn down in sections, 3 feet at a time.

The largest NTC poles in the United Kingdom were two 85-foot stout H-poles carrying heavy-gauge copper wires over the River Ouse at Godmanchester, near Huntingdon.

The NTC also left the POED a great legacy of heavy-gauge underground copper cable, but the passing of the years has stuck much of it fast in its ducts, defying anything modern engineering techniques can contrive to get it out of the ground. A great wealth of asset has thus been transferred onward to BT in a good, appreciating asset which can never, it seems, be realised economically.

All the "old boys" whom I and my colleagues succeeded in 1947 had lived through the Great Slump of the 20s and 30s. This was a desperate and brutal period for them and their families. A large proportion of the established staff of the POED were laid off temporarily without pay, while the national economy fell into deep recession after World War 1. Indeed, these men had only recently fought for King and Country in the appalling conditions of the war and, having survived it, an achievement in itself, were obliged to survive a longer period on the dole before re-engagement by the POED. I was told of many hardships which befell relatively well-qualified POED staff at that time.

However, such problems were as nothing compared with the capital risk ventures in Telephony which had swept Britain at the turn of the 20th century. Telegraphy by Morse over wires (hence the term "Telegraph Pole", still in use) had been established as early as 1865. The telegraph service, manifesting itself to the public as Telegrams, was taken over by the Post Office on 28 January 1870 while, with true British reserve, declining to take up Alexander Graham Bell's telephone patents when offered about that time. Sir William Preece, the Post Office Engineer-in-Chief of the day was, however, impressed by the potential of the invention of telephonic voice transmission, and lent support to a modest amount of research so that the Post Office could launch into this new technology with more confidence at a later date. In fact, the first Post Office public telephone exchange opened at Swansea on 23 March 1881, followed by others at Newcastle upon Tyne and Middlesbrough.

There was no monopoly at that stage, and the highly successful NTC extended its substantial network through the length and breadth of the land, into the 20th century. It was around the turn of the century that the meteoric rise in the number of telephones in Britain led to numerous competing risk ventures, most of which had little in the way of a firm foundation or research backup. Local authorities had to oversee such companies, but few made it, and many crashed.

Six local authorities formed telephone departments themselves, following an enabling Act of Parliament in 1899, with subsidies from local and national taxation funds. In order of opening these were Glasgow (April 1901), Tunbridge Wells (July 1901), Swansea (September 1902), Portsmouth (November 1902), Brighton (October 1903) and Hull (October 1904).

As the fierce competition for subscribers grew and political pressure to transfer the network into public ownership increased, even the larger companies ran into difficulties, and firms such as the previously successful United Telephone Company were merged with the NTC to avoid disaster.

Around 1905, the operating companies began to realise what they had started, and the need for an ever-increasing network of Junction lines between their exchanges became obvious from customer demands. Clearly none of the companies or municipalities could cope with the size of the giant they had created, and the ongoing debate came to a head in Parliament, requiring the POED to take them all over. The eventual parliamentary decision in 1905 set the scene for this arrangement and in 1912, after ratification of the detail by Parliament to give system unification with the POED, the NTC succumbed. So started the long mopping-up process of the remaining private and local authority networks by the POED - all, that is, except Hull Corporation, which has stuck out adamantly ever since, and seems likely to carry its small network into the 21st century, albeit now Kingston Communications plc.

It should be recognised, however, that Hull has enjoyed many goodwill relationships with the POED, and subsequently with BT departments, but the commercial severity of BT's operating licence can no longer allow support for such luxuries. At the time of floating BT on the London Stock Market in 1984 I was personally responsible for informing the Telephone Manager of Hull Corporation that BT could no longer negotiate exchange equipment contracts for Hull free of agency charge. Kingston Communications plc now has to absorb the cost of such functions or do the job itself.

So, apart from Hull, the process of handover to the POED was virtually complete by 1912, and a whole new story had begun, integrating local exchange switching with the concept of a Trunk and Junction network under unified control, allowing integrated national standards to be applied, not to mention a national tariff structure. The solidly-built NTC plant gave a fine starting impetus.

At this stage all exchanges were manual, but Almon Brown Strowger, an American undertaker with more than usual imagination, had already on 12 March 1899 set the seeds of telephone switching mechanisation by patenting in the USA an electro-mechanical "step-by-step" exchange, which he invented mainly to prevent a relation of a competitor, who was the telephone operator, from losing him business.

The British Post Office again showed interest, and in 1912 opened a trial Strowger exchange, Britain's first automated system, at Epsom, as forerunner to the near-total conversion to Strowger by the late 1950s. This development was, however, painfully slow compared with progress in the USA, where many

*A CBS2 Exchange*

*A CB10 Manual Switchboard*

automatic exchanges were in use before 1900. Several developers had, in fact, built their own automatic exchange types in the USA and Canada, so it was no surprise that the POED opened trial versions of the Canadian Machine Telephone Company, and Western Electric, exchanges at Hereford and Darlington respectively later in 1914. Other experimental variants were tried in Britain up to World War 2, but the standard generally accepted was the Strowger type.

The Strowger system has been much maligned for its high maintenance costs and slow operation, but it should be said in its favour that the Strowger era lasted in Britain for two-thirds of the century, and has seen the network grow from its modest beginnings to the saturated penetration of the 90s, to be ousted first by the much shorter-lasting Crossbar and so-called Electronic exchange systems, and then by Digital systems, ie, software-based systems which align, only just in time, with the Data boom of the late century.

As the network grew from 1900 to 1914, so the construction and maintenance of lines had to be managed and organised. The POED had no commercial motor vehicles in those days, and gangs carried their poles to site on pole carts, pulled by Shire horses and manoeuvred on site by hand. Maintenance linemen also located and attended their faults on horseback or on foot, with much tedium and ineffective time.

So in 1914, inevitably, the quest for efficiency and economy led to a case being made by the POED Controller of Supplies for the acquisition of motor-cycles and sidecars for Linemen in rural areas. Earlier a case for bicycles for use in the remoter parts of Scotland had been rejected. After much debate, fine budgeting and flow of correspondence, the motor-cycle contract was placed in 1916.

After World War 1, surplus heavy Army lorries were offered for sale and, as an experiment, the POED purchased a handful of them for carrying stores, to supplement the steam tractor already operating at the Supplies Department at Mount Pleasant, London.

In the 1930s, however, it became apparent that the POED, now armed with a growing library of standard procedures for the construction and maintenance of overhead and underground lines in the form of Engineering Instructions, could specify the types of vehicles needed by Cable Jointers and Linemen. Contracts were placed with Morris and Morris Commercial respectively for Linemen's vans and Jointers' vehicles. The purpose-built Linemen's vans had an angled pane of glass above the windscreen to allow the Lineman to inspect the route of wires for faults as he drove slowly along - a practice which would undoubtedy be considered unsafe in the 1990s. The special feature of the Jointer's van was the purpose-built exterior side cupboards for stowing jointing stores.

Still the gangs had no purpose-built vehicle until, just before World War 2, Albion developed the first Overhead Construction vehicle - a rather ponderous narrow affair with over-light springing for the job, which made it roll alarmingly in use. But to the gangs they were luxury indeed, if very late in coming. These vehicles were made at the Albion works at Bathgate, Scotland, and the first of its type to enter the POED yard at Ipswich was driven by its gang driver all the way from the North. The assembled staff waited and waited for it to arrive and, at last, some 3 hours late, it swung into the yard in a great plume of steam. It was not until later that the driver was informed that the van had a fourth gear!

By 1980 the Post Office Telecommunications transport fleet had grown to 44,000 vehicles, the largest fleet in Britain and probably in Europe.

Earlier I mentioned the development of Morse telegraphy over wires by the 1860s. In hindsight, the developments from Alexander Graham Bell's analogue (ie, "uncoded") voice transmission telephony principle, which appeared largely to replace Telegraphy in the progression of the Industry, could be regarded as the great mis-timed event of the 20th century.

In the 1980s and 1990s, automatic Telephone Exchange switching and transmission are being universally "digitised", coding speech into telegraphic form, so returning to a higher-technology version of Telegraph transmission. The commercial development of solid state integrated circuits using silicon chips in the 1960s and 1970s, mainly to facilitate the rapid growth of the Computer Industry, was at the root of this change of direction in Telephony.

So, when most automatic telephone exchanges in the World, and certainly all in Britain, are replaced by Digital units in the next few years, a line will be drawn under the Analogue Telephony era which has lasted for over a century.

Not that Telegraphy died completely in that long period. Far from it, as the customer still demanded non-voice services and facilities, with particular emphasis on the direct transmission of typed messages and, later, whole pages of typescript, in the form of Telegrams and Telex. This was necessitated partly by the slowness of development of the commercial use of thermionic valves for amplification of voice circuits over about 15 miles in length, which placed a restriction on long-distance telephony until well into the 1920s. Again, it was another developing sister industry which set the pace in this technology as the Radio Broadcast business was born out of Marconi's famous early transmission across the Bristol Channel. The POED's parallel development of valve amplifiers for line transmission led to the formal evolution of the British telephone Trunk and Junction networks. Developments such as this were of such importance that the POED set up its own Engineering Research establishment at Dollis Hill, in North London.

The earliest Telegrams were sent over wires in the mid-19th century, in the form of Wheatstone's Automatic Telegraph System in 1858. They were re-transmitted around every 15 miles, with de-coding at the destination into a written document for personal delivery by Post Office staff.

In 1874, J.M.E. Baudot, a French engineer, invented and introduced an automatic printing telegraph system, with sending and receiving equipment which eventually replaced Morse by a new 5-element code, allowing a transmission speed of 35 words per minute.

In later development the POED adopted a refinement of the Baudot code designed by Murray, but Baudot was immortalised by the creation of the international unit still known as the Baud, representing code elements transmitted per second.

The larger Telegraph Offices used typescript, and there is little doubt that this combination of circumstances led to a number of patents being lodged, following the invention of electric typewriters with telegraphic coding facilities. By far the earliest of these was invented in 1912 by a cold storage engineer called Henry Krum, in Chicago. Building much later on this principle the POED introduced, around 1925, a machine developed by Krum's resultant company, Morkrum, transmitting at 40 words per minute, and known in Britain as the Teleprinter no. 1A.

Despite the Great Slump and its effects on the take-up of new developments, this was an exciting period for Telecommunications, and a radio-telephone circuit, facilitated by current radio development and the thermionic valve, opened between London and New York. In 1928, a Teletype developed by Creed was used over this link, transmitting at 65 words per minute or 50 bauds. Earlier, during World War 1, telegraphic links had been established between Britain and the near Continent, using heavy-gauge Submarine Cables with longer unamplified section lengths than would normally be economic for inland transmission.

The great advantage of Telegraphy over Telephony was that much lower transmission quality was required to detect the on-off current alternations of the telegraphic codes than that needed to detect coherent speech, a principle exploited also in the present-day digitisation of transmitted speech and music.

By 1932, two other significant developments had occurred. First, the Teleprinter no. 7 had been developed by Creed to send a page of typescript, albeit line-by-line, and secondly the Amplifier no. 32, a thermionic valve amplifier developed by Dollis Hill for inland Trunk and Junction lines, had become standard POED equipment. It was then a short step to adapt the telegraphic on-off code idea to interrupt voice-frequency tones capable of amplification on telephony circuits. This development of Voice Frequency (VF) Telegraphy set the scene for what was to become the post-World War 2 data telecommunications boom.

My apprenticeship period from 1947 to 1949 was, indeed, pivotal. After finishing my External Works training, I was moved to the Colchester Telegraph Office where, in 1948, a Phonogram service was operating in a back room of the Head Post Office, where telegraph operators received phoned-in Telegrams from the public, and hand-written Telegrams from the Post Office counter. These were typed by the operators and then sent over direct teleprinter lines by means of Teleprinters no. 7 and VF lines for delivery or onward manual relayed transmission at the distant end.

My work entailed the routine maintenance of the Teleprinters. The daily replacement of the messy felt rollers known as Inkers sticks particularly in my memory. I remember also being enthralled by the electro-mechanical complexity of the Teleprinter no. 7, so the rumoured demise of the developer in a mental hospital was hardly surprising to me.

The same could not be said about Alexander Graham Bell's telephone instrument, whose simple carbon granule microphone and moving coil receiver remained virtually unchanged through the first 75 years, the only refinements being the improvement of technical quality, changed external appearance and the introduction of dials to signal the customers' intent to the emerging automatic exchanges. Indeed, the merging of the early "candlestick" separate transmitter and receiver into a combined handset was seen by many as a retrograde step when telephoned messages needed to be written down by the user.

# Chapter 2

# *The Strowger Era*

From the 1930s, the POED's Research Station at Dollis Hill developed a highly structured approach to Research and Development of Telephonic and Telegraphic Network Engineering. The work lay in two main segments, Transmission and Exchange Systems.

The use of Strowger and the other automatic exchange systems since 1912 gave the research and development engineers much food for thought as to how the network should be developed and controlled. Despite the dominance then of manual systems such as the Central Battery Systems nos. 1 and 10 (CB1 and CB10) in British towns, and the Central Battery Signalling System no. 2 (CBS2) in rural areas, a long programme of total automation using the Strowger system was embarked upon. The system conversion programme got off to rather a spluttering start with the advent of World War 2, so freezing most jobs for 6 years.

The criteria for determining which exchanges featured in the priority-order programme were both interesting and complex. Telephone penetration grew rapidly at the end of the war, and many of the manual exchanges faced short-term exhaustion. With the POED firmly under Civil Service control, Opposition politicians were quick to complain about exchange exhaustions and growing waiting lists for service (especially for emergency cases such as doctors' lines), so high-level complaints from customers, known as Flag Cases, mainly politically generated, or cases likely to develop, were very seriously regarded by local POED managers. Conversely, such real and potential political cases carried much weight in District Engineers' competing bids to the Engineer-in-Chief's Office for their share of the development capital budget. Another variable in this situation was the amount of spare space in manual exchange buildings, often making it more economic and expeditious to extend the manual switchboard rather than replace it with a Strowger exchange. Such manual extensions were fairly commonplace right up to the mid-60s. Where the building was inadequate to extend the contained system, the cost of the new Strowger had to be increased by the building costs. Some conversion schemes had to be delayed (thus causing Flag Cases and questions in Parliament) when difficulties arose over planning agreements with the local authorities because, for both technical and cost reasons, the new buildings had to be located in town centres.

In some cases the POED had to accept that there was no ready solution so, ever

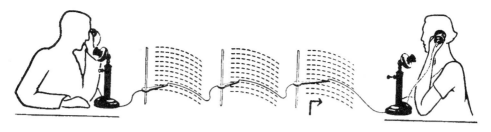

*The "Step-by-Step" Strowger System*

*A Uniselector Linefinder in a Strowger Exchange*

*A typical large exchange Cable Chamber*

*A Strowger 2-Motion Selector*

*Subscribers' Meters in an Automatic Exchange*

*A Distribution Frame in a Strowger Exchange*

*An Auto-Manual Centre (AMC)*

*A rural Unit Automatic Exchange (UAX)*

41

resourceful, Dollis Hill brought in the expedient of Shared Service, developed out of the old manual Party Line concept. Not until the long post-war boom diminished did the POED's successor organisations carry out de-sharing programmes to eradicate this unsatisfactory expedient.

Another good argument for automating exchanges was the potential reduction of running costs and fault rates. This applied mainly to rural areas, where small CBS2 manual switchboards abounded before World War 2 behind village Post Office counters, and in the front rooms of private houses. To alleviate this costly arrangement, Dollis Hill adapted the Strowger system into various types of Unit Automatic Exchange (UAXs) which were introduced in a substantial automation programme throughout the rural areas of the UK before and after the war. These little exchanges, which could be enlarged as required by the provision of additional "units", proved to be highly successful, and some (especially the UAX 13s with 200 lines) are still in use after 50 years operation.

All public exchanges must tolerate and function under the most stringent line conditions connected to them, so with the issue of each successive new Strowger variant, Local Line Planning Engineers had to be issued with Transmission (ie Speech) and Signalling (ie Ringing etc) limits, outside which individual connected lines would not work. Broadly, the replaced manual exchanges would tolerate worse lines, so the positioning of the new Strowger units in the optimum Economic Centre always formed a crucial initial study before an exchange conversion.

The POED had always had the option of providing or extending exchanges by means of its own Construction workforce or by contract, and this proved to be an excellent means of controlling manpower numbers in the post-war peaks and troughs of network expansion, often caused by minor short-term "stop-go" features in the national economy. A common pattern was the construction and commissioning of large urban Strowgers by contractors such as AEI (and later Plessey, STC and GEC), and the extension of manual exchanges and UAXs by POED direct labour. Small enhancements to all units were usually done by POED direct labour.

My own involvement in this process, late in my apprenticeship, lay in the extension of the UAX 13 exchanges at Long Melford and Clare, in Suffolk, working with my Technical Officer to schematic and wiring diagrams, and taking responsibility for the efficient working of each exchange on completion of the job, and above all preserving an efficient standard of service for the customers during the period of work. In these remote rural units, the Technical Officer and his Apprentice were very much on their own, having to rely on their own resources and initiative to ensure that Dollis Hill's methods worked in practice.

The local Maintenance Technical Officer would call in to test faulty lines and equipment, so giving us an insight into engineering problems from a different viewpoint, and other staff such as Cable Jointers and Telephone Fitters also had occasion to visit. The brilliantly simple Detector no. 4, a sort of universal voltmeter, played a major role in everyone's work.

The maintenance man was broadly responsible for 5 or 6 UAXs and their total of 1,000 or so lines, so giving him the added role of POED representative to his customers. As I found when carrying out leave relief work for Maintenance Technical Officers a year or two later, this responsibility called for much diplomacy, especially when customers felt that they were getting less than satisfactory service. For as long as I have been associated with telephone exchange operation, a proportion of customers have claimed that they are being overcharged, and whoever was working in the exchange at the time of queries was asked to check the relevant meters, both to confirm the readings and to verify correct operation. The option of meters at the customer's house or office was introduced much later. Meter query cases were rarely found to be justified, and more often than not teenage members of the family had been using the telephone without their parents' knowledge. Some customers were also very demanding, and the Headmistress of the day at the Colchester County High School for Girls was well known for giving telephone maintenance staff a rough time with complaints, real and imagined. Between my periods of rural maintenance relief and construction work in the larger Strowger exchange at Colchester, I was often sent by the Maintenance Control or Test Desk to service the lines at the High School for Girls. I always found that the lady responded charmingly to a polite and, hopefully, effective approach.

The construction work at the large Strowger units usually involved large amounts of new cabling, using the best available types of cable in the pre-plastic insulation era, that is, cable with braided cotton insulation round the wires, each with its own colour code. Once stripped, the cable ends had to be dipped in hot molten beeswax to prevent the insulation from fraying. When carrying the wax bowl from the heater to the job, often at ceiling level over the equipment, it was essential to shout "Hot Wax!" at every blind corner in the equipment racks, to avoid accidents. Connection of the wires to the equipment with long-nosed pliers know as "81s" was a skilled art, as was the soldering of them without causing "dry joints" due to flux running from an underheated soldering iron.

As the network grew after World War 2, Dollis Hill foresaw the unacceptable features of the original, slow Strowger equipment, and so designed and trialled a system using faster-acting relays, called the 2000-type. All previous Strowger equipment was from that time known as pre-2000-type. The two system variants lived together for several years, often in the same exchanges, but by the 60s, the same replacement programme which phased out the manual exchanges got rid of most of the pre-2000-type equipment as well.

A later 4000-type improved the system still further in some units.

A feature of the larger Strowger exchanges was the facility of automatic routine testing of lines and equipment at night, when telephone traffic was low, and automatic indication of fault conditions, for clearing in the morning before the start of the busy hour. Automatic traffic recorders also showed on meters how many calls passed through each part of the exchange, thus giving the Planning Engineers as early warning as possible as to where the equipment or cabling needed to be supplemented.

The very existence of the exchange as a central point in the network (the Continental word for Exchange is Centrale) provided a convenient point to test each customer's line, on the Main Distribution Frame where the lines entering from the street are cross-connected to the exchange switching equipment. The manned Test Desk was usually co-sited with these test points, and later developments allowed for the Test Technicians to test the equipment and lines at the remote unmanned UAXs "parented" on the large exchange, by remote control.

Although not a feature of my own formative years, the POED staff in the Strowger exchanges in the big cities such as London, Birmingham and Manchester were very proud of the Director System, a special networking Strowger system for quick inter-exchange connection on local calls across the city, and characterised by letter-and-figure dials on the telephones enabling alpha-numeric telephone numbers such as WHI 1212 for Whitehall 1212. Even early on in the development of this system in London the effects of rapid network growth on the strategy were felt, when it became necessary to invent some meaningless exchange names such as SPEedwell, as letter combinations ran out. Much later, London bewailed the passing of letter dials in favour of the now-essential national numeric numbering scheme.

The Strowger system represented the major revolution in Automatic Telephony in the UK, and because it tended to be somewhat labour-intensive, many labour-saving features were developed and introduced during its currency. Strowger relays tended to go out of adjustment after a longish period of use, and Exchange Routine Maintenance staff toured each exchange in turn, to readjust and lubricate all items on a set timetable. However, many years later, in the late 60s, the sciences of Value Analysis and Work Study began to question the value of Routine Preventative Maintenance, and trials, leading to a new standard procedure, were carried out to deal with each equipment fault as it happened, recording and analysing each event, as an alternative to the expensive maintenance tour. But by then the new, faster systems to replace Strowger were already on the drawing board.

All I have mentioned about the Strowger system relates to the switching of calls between telephones using rotary dials (which, themselves, were notorious for going out of adjustment), but coincidentally the older Telegraph systems had themselves undergone research and development, and line switching between customers' teleprinters had evolved in the form of the Telex service, also using modified Strowger equipment, in special Telex exchange units and networks. They were maintained by specialist staff dual-trained in Telephonic and Telegraphic engineering.

Until well into the 50s, the automation programme by means of Strowger still addressed only local and junction calls. All Trunk and International calls had to be routed via the new centralised manual switchboards associated with the principal urban Strowger units, known as Auto-Manual Centres. The operators at these switchboards also handled, courteously, queries from customers, Directory Enquiries and 999 Emergency calls. Although 999 took longer to dial than, say, 111, there was much more risk of false alarms with 111, partially due to the wind tapping overhead wires together, as such conditions would simulate the loop-disconnect signals normally produced by a dial, and partly for other technical reasons.

Auto-Manual Centre (AMC) operators connecting call office calls were trained to recognise the different sounds made by each denomination of coin as it went into the coinbox. All other long-distance calls were charged by the AMC operators writing charging tickets.

Maybe a salutary epitaph to the Strowger era can be derived from the unforgivable surprise visit by my family to a 90-year-old relation in the late 70s, when the Strowger phase-out programme was getting under way. "But my dears", protested this aristocratic lady, "I have nothing in to give you for tea". Then the miracle happened. She went to her telephone, dialled 100, and said to the AMC operator at Reading "This is Miss Beck at Henley. Please connect me with my Grocer". To my amazement, within seconds, she was ordering sliced ham from the Grocer round the corner. Miss Beck, clearly, was documented on each Reading AMC position, with all her tradespeople listed. She explained "I never could get used to this dial thing", and accepted nothing less than the personal service she came to expect from the Manual system which was replaced 40 years earlier!

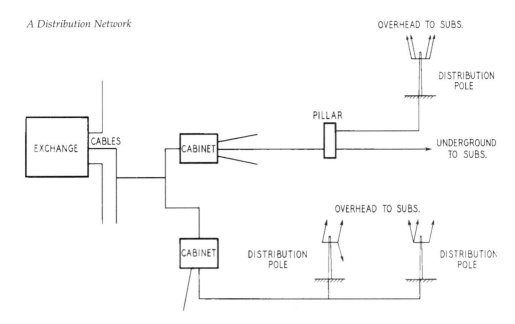

OVERHEAD TO SUBS.

DISTRIBUTION POLE

PILLAR

EXCHANGE    CABLES    CABINET

UNDERGROUND TO SUBS.

OVERHEAD TO SUBS.

CABINET    DISTRIBUTION POLE    DISTRIBUTION POLE

*Regulating Dropwire to Subscribers' premises*

*Local Underground Network Cable Jointing in a large Development Scheme*

47

# Chapter 3

# *The Lines and the Network*

Back we go to the end of October 1958. As Circuit Provision Control Assistant Executive Engineer at the Cambridge Telephone Area, I received advice that Mr R.D. Norton, the Court Postmaster of the day had, as always, requested connection of the Royal Private Telephone Circuit and the Royal Teleprinter Circuit from Sandringham House to Buckingham Palace for the annual visit by Her Majesty the Queen and the Royal Family. However, this year a new feature appeared, a vision circuit to enable Her Majesty to broadcast her Christmas message live by Television.

In the company of a senior member of the Area Maintenance staff, I went to Sandringham for the preliminary survey, only to find that under no circumstances would the Sandringham Estate Manager contemplate vision cables trailing out of the Long Library windows while Her Majesty was in residence. Nor would he underwrite the cost of new permanent vision cables, as this was the first time a vision broadcast had been tried from Sandringham House.

I was well acquainted with the Vision Outside Broadcast vehicle crews from London, who also co-operated with the Cambridge Area on the live annual Christmas Broadcast of the Service of Nine Lessons and Carols from King's College Chapel, Cambridge. So we tried an experiment. Between us, we negotiated that the Outside Broadcast vehicle could stand about 200 yards from Sandringham House, at a point where the ordinary telephone cables passed under the paths of the garden. We found a spare pair of wires in a cable, and attempted to send a test vision signal over it. The telephone cable was designed to accept voice frequency only, but at the required 4 megahertz for sending a picture we were exceeding the design characteristics 1000-fold. Our hopes were based on the shortness of the link — and it worked. I doubt if an outside vision broadcast of this importance was ever designed on such a shaky basis, and we were very conscious that every set in the country would be tuned in to the first televised formal Christmas message by Her Majesty. However, we were old hands at providing the Sound circuit, which would broadcast the message to 220 million people throughout the world.

There is a theory that the Cambridge Telephone Area included North-West Norfolk so that a single management could control the Christmas Broadcast from Sandringham to London. Back in the early days of the BBC, POED maintenance staff were stationed at the tops of strategic poles in case of failure.

Having dined on the full Christmas Dinner provided by the Sandringham Estate Manager, we crowded into the shoe-box of a Control Room under the Long Library, watching our monitor set for the picture via London to appear, as 3 pm approached. Panic set in when, after 15 seconds, no picture appeared, but the big sigh of relief came after 20 seconds when the Queen appeared on the screen and the Broadcast started perfectly. I learned later that a BBC technician connected the circuit 20 seconds late in Broadcasting House. We never did this again, as Her Majesty has opted for pre-taped messages ever since.

While on the subject of Vision Broadcasts, I found myself in 1969 in charge of the Eastern Region Network Co-Ordination Centre at Colchester, covering major breakdown restoration in about one-tenth of the UK. The first-ever dedicated TV cable had been laid under the A41 road from London to Birmingham. A Post Office Engineering Inspector phoned me to ask permission to cut the TV cable, which was suspended 15 feet above the High Street at Tring, Herts, having been brought up on the bucket of a mechanical roadworks digger. I checked with the TV Control Room in London, to find that a perfect picture was being networked live over the cable, and so I instructed the Inspector to rope off the area, and let nobody even breathe on the cable until the transmission had ended.

But all this is the spectacular aspect of Line Transmission. The real bread and butter of the POED was the Public Telephone Network, in all its forms — Local, Junction and Trunk Lines, using Physical, Carrier or Radio links, all matched to the various conditions required by the Exchange types to which they were connected.

Of the old Magneto System, early in this century, it was said that a call could be made even with one wire severed and touching the ground. The same cannot be said of the later more sophisticated exchange systems, which necessitated a far more disciplined approach to network design, both as regards signalling and the transmission of speech. I have a personal debt of gratitude to the new science of network design in the 1950s, as I was allocated as a Technician to Local Line Planning in the Colchester Telephone Area when I was demobilised from National Service in 1952, and rose, via Technical Officer, to Assistant Executive Engineer on the same discipline at Reading in 1956. During those 4 years, I was wholly or partly responsible for the local network developments at Colchester West, Ipswich Docks, Framlingham, Reading (Tilehurst), Wokingham and Ascot. The work at Reading in 1956/57 was hard and intensive, as we strove to narrow the gap between the over-buoyant post-war demand for telephones in the expanding town, and the flat-out rate of planning and installing the network. At one stage there was a Waiting List of 2,500 lines in Reading alone.

But soon I was off to pastures new, and took on the mixed load of Area Training Officer, Circuit Provision Control and Area Stores Control Officer at Cambridge. The Cambridge Area Engineer of the day, Clifford Riley, was probably the biggest single influence on my subsequent managerial development. He told me a network anecdote relating to his own return to Cambridge on promotion from the Bedford Area, one calm Summer evening just after the war. Clifford had been RAF Liaison Officer at Cambridge during the war, and so knew the local cable network in great detail. He opened his new office window, overlooking Regent Street, to cool the room, and heard a rather earthy conversation floating up from an open telephone manhole in the street, 3 floors below. "Well I say that **** cable is Cable Code W". "Don't be **** daft, I know that this **** cable is W". "Get **** lost...." etc, etc. Clifford slipped on an old mac and went down the stairs, out into the street, and down the manhole. "That's **** Cable Code W", he told them "How do you **** know ?" "I just do. Open the **** cable up, and you'll **** well see." With that, he returned to his office and listened to the end of the conversation. "Well, **** me ! That **** bloke was right ! Who was he ?" "**** if I know, but cor, don't 'e swear !"

When Clifford retired, after a period of 16 years as Area Engineer, I paid a routine training visit to an overhead construction gang near Cambridge. Tom Yates, the foreman, said that he was missing the regular morale-boosting field visits from Mr Riley, and asked when I thought his successor would start going into the field. I did not have the heart to say that he never would.

My network responsibilities widened while at Cambridge, and as engineer in charge of Circuit Provision, I now had to arrange the provision of Public Trunk and Junction circuits to satisfy the Area Schedule of Circuit Estimates, worked out by the seemingly mysterious group of statisticians known as the Traffic Division. Trunk circuit allocation was strictly controlled from the Headquarters Long Lines Division at Brogyntyn Hall, Oswestry, and I and my colleagues often met the engineers from there when they visited Cambridge. Following the inauguration of Subscriber Trunk Dialling (STD) by Her Majesty the Queen at Bristol in 1959, this facility was extended systematically throughout the UK by the creation of a network of high-grade Strowger exchanges specifically for switching trunk calls, known as Zone Centres. These units were linked to each other by zero-loss 4-wire circuits with rapid signal regeneration.

A typical Zone Centre was the unit at Long Road, Cambridge, which, at the centre of East Anglia, was connected to the Group Switching Centres (GSCs) throughout the Zone, like the spokes of a wheel. This exchange was cut into the network in 1963, so relieving much trunk pressure from London, as did the other two new Zone Centres at Reading and Tunbridge Wells. My Circuit Provision duty was the focal point for the detailed planning of the Cambridge Zone Centre, in close co-operation with the Installation Engineers and Oswestry.

STD came to the Cambridge Area quite early on, the first STD exchange in the Area being Newmarket. The Assistant Postmaster-General of the day, Miss Mervyn Pike, came to open the new service, and the Mayor of Newmarket opted to make the inaugural STD call to Mrs Mirabelle Topham at that other great racing centre, Aintree. The time for the changeover to STD was set for 1 pm, a time of light traffic. None of the dignitaries knew that the dialling of the call was actually a facade, as we had arranged a special private circuit in advance, with another in reserve. At 12.50 pm, the word came to the Circuit Provision Control that a fault had developed on the first private circuit, in Birmingham. I activated the reserve circuit via Leicester, only to find that, at

*H.M. The Queen inaugurating the Subscriber Trunk Dialling (STD) Service at Bristol*

12.55 pm, someone working on roadworks in the Midlands had dug up the cable. A very anxious member of the Traffic Division, speaking in hushed tones from Newmarket, asked me what to do. I suggested that all Miss Pike could do in the circumstances was to dial Mrs Topham over the real network. It worked perfectly, but none of the smiling faces at each end of the connection knew anything of the 10-minute drama acted out in the "back room" in Cambridge.

As the STD network grew, the Strowger Trunk Exchanges were replaced by high-speed Crossbar switching units, but soon even they were insufficient to cope with the surging increase in traffic. To prevent "overflows" on trunk traffic, an overlaid supplementary trunk switched network was installed, with 37 strategically placed exchanges throughout the UK, known as the Transit Network. Calls which could not get through the normal routing due to congestion or switching complexity were randomly switched into the Transit Network, so that a call from London to Scotland could, say, be routed via York or Preston. This meant that at the Preston Transit unit the maintenance staff would know that heavy traffic was passing through, but would have no idea of its sources or destinations. Real automation of the network had arrived. In 1979 I found myself as Head of a Management Services Group in Headquarters in London, developing on-line computer maintenance facilities for the Transit Switching units, as a result of which the unsuccessful call attempt rate dropped from 8% to 2%, this lower figure being due to customer error.

*The POED Cable Ship Monarch IV. She was replaced in 1975 by Monarch V, which is still in service with BT*

*The First Officer of a Cable-Ship has the task of detecting when the Grappling Iron has found the Cable on the sea-bed by sitting on the rope on which the Grappling-Iron is suspended*

*A marker buoy being lowered after cable laying*

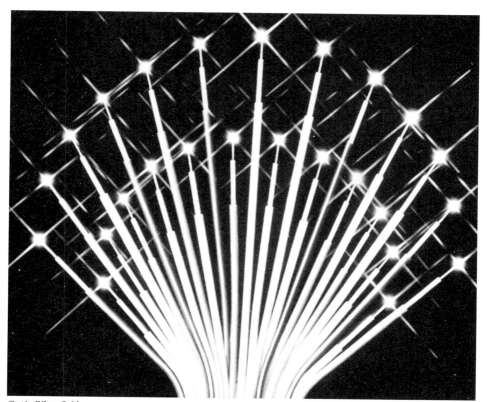

*Optic Fibre Cable*

Developments in Trunk Switching were matched by developments in Line System technology, in which nearly 1,000 conversations were multiplexed on to a single pair of coaxial conductors. DC power, fed out on the central conductor, powered intermediate solid-state amplifiers along the route. These systems could be used either for telephony or the sending of a TV picture — a far cry from our Heath Robinson effort at Sandringham in 1958. Due to the very high risks attached to accidental damage to these cable systems, and the need to plan routine disconnections carefully, the Network Co-ordination Centre system was introduced.

Coincident with these developments in inland communications, Carrier Multiplexing was also brought into use on Submarine Cable transmission, continuing the POED's long tradition of being in the forefront of Submarine Cable technology, exemplified by the fleet of Post Office Cable Ships used by telecommunications authorities all over the world. In the case of submarine cables, the relatively inaccessible nature of the submerged amplifiers meant that a long life had to be built into the equipment, necessitating the use of gold plating on all the component parts.

Another technology which came to fruition in the 1960s was Air Pressurisation of cables. This principle, by which compressed air or nitrogen inside a cable sheath holds out water in ducts and manholes and therefore prevents faults, was first considered in the 30s, but not until nearly 30 years later could it be realised, as telecommunications had to wait for the development of a resin for the cable ends which did not contract on cooling. Clifford Riley was quick to see the advantages of Air Pressurisation, and used the national field trial in the Cambridge Area to make his network watertight, making his Area the envy of the whole country.

*The POED's first 5 Vehicles*

*Transporting Stout Poles*

*Moving a Stout Pole on to a Pole Cart at the work site*

*The Albion Gang Vehicle*

*Artists' impression of an Albion in use*

*Erecting a Medium Pole with Ladders. 1940s*

*A Simon Pole Erection Unit*

*A King Pole Erection Unit*

# Chapter 4

# *Post Office and British Telecom Transport*

The Telegram Service was introduced before 1897, but up to that date the radius for free delivery was 1 mile. In 1897, as part of Queen Victoria's Diamond Jubilee concessions, the radius for free delivery of telegrams was extended to 3 miles and, at the same time, daily delivery of letters was introduced. The Engineer-in-Chief, realising that local mobility was called for to operate these improved services, requested that the Controller of Telegraph Stores should order 100 Trade Patent cycles from the Quadrant Cycle Co. Ltd. These were obtained but were found to be rather unsatisfactory for use by Postmen, due to their poor quality, but the experiment established the principle of the use of wheeled transport for Post Office staff mobility.

Building on this early start, improved cycles were subsequently provided for Telegraph Linesmen to considerable advantage, and there is no doubt that their provision was a significant aid towards the efficient maintenance of the increasing number of telegraph lines throughout Britain. By 1909, more than 5,000 Postmen were using bicycles, carrier-tricycles and bicycles with trailer-carts, while 750 Telegraph Linesmen went about their official duties by cycle.

By 1903, responsibility for the provision of Post Office bicycles was transferred from the POED to the Post Office Stores Dept., shortly after which a Stores Transport Dept. was formed, under the leadership of a Major C. Wheeler. Major Wheeler was responsible for preparing a high contract specification for the "Standard Bicycle", to ensure that the old problems of poor quality did not persist as the numbers of machines in the field grew. Since the Post Office was a major user of bicycles at that time, it is undoubted that the high standard of the contract specification contributed in no small part to the success of British bicycles on the World market.

During the early years of the 20th century, the Stores Transport Dept. was called upon to provide and handle more and more items of stores, thus providing Major Wheeler with an ever-increasing problem as to how to handle the heavy work at the Mount Pleasant Depot, such as the conveyance of large amounts of cable. Motorised traction was in its infancy, and various exhibitions were staged by manufacturers to advertise their vehicles. In November 1904, the Stores Transport Dept. decided to hire a vehicle for use at Mount Pleasant for an experimental period of 4 weeks. This vehicle was a Steam Tractor, manufactured and hired by Wallis & Stevens of Basingstoke. The trial was a resounding success, leading to the eventual purchase of the Steam Tractor during the latter half of 1905, the first self-propelled vehicle ever to enter Post Office service. Its capital cost was £430, and the estimated running costs were £26 6s 8d per month, which showed a healthy saving on the customary horse hire of £37 per month, a cost advantage which persuaded the responsible Secretary at the Treasury to approve the purchase. The Steam Tractor was eventually sold in 1914, after constant use on stores handling, for a price of £200. So far as I know, this was the only steam propelled road vehicle ever owned by the Post Office. However, it demonstrated that the running costs of a self-propelled vehicle compared favourably with horse hire. This led, in 1906, to the purchase of the first petrol-driven vehicle for Post Office use. It is interesting to note that, while the Wallis & Stevens steam tractor performed successfully during its initial 4 weeks trial in 1904, a Thorneycroft petrol-driven lorry, hired for 2 weeks in the same period, was not as successful, being dogged by breakdowns thoughout its trial. This comparative success of steam traction undoubtedly delayed the introduction of petrol-driven vehicles into the Post Office by 2 years.

In the Winter of 1905/6, the Stores Transport Dept. hired a petrol-driven 2 tonne Maudsley lorry for carrying light stores items. This vehicle showed improvement over the earlier experiments with internal combustion engined vehicles, and it was soon proved that the Maudsley achieved a consistent saving of 30% compared with hiring horses. After this proving period the Maudsley was purchased, and put into service in London in January 1907. This vehicle bore the serial "No. 1". It gave economic and trouble-free service until 1925, when it was sold back to its manufacturers, who used it as a publicity vehicle. During its 18 years of Post Office service it was driven approximately 300,000 miles.

Up to 1906, senior staff of the POED made their official journeys by horse and cart, trap, gig, and official bicycle. In 1906, the Sectional Engineer, Gloucester, was privileged to be issued with the first motor car of the POED, in which he drove himself on all his subsequent official business journeys.

With the exception of the Wallis & Stevens steam tractor and the Maudsley lorry, the Stores Transport Dept. made do with hired vehicles until 1910, when 3 additional vehicles were bought, namely a Ryknield, a Halley and an Alldays & Onions. In 1914, the stores fleet was supplemented by a further 5 Alldays & Onions 30 cwt vehicles, and in 1915 by a Napier 30 cwt and 2 Maudsley 4 tonne vehicles. By 1923 the Stores Fleet had grown to 36 vehicles, covering approximately 230,000 miles per annum. The breakdown rate of 25 in 1921 dropped progressively to 8 in 1923, during which time the fleet grew from 31 to 36.

Specialist vehicles began to emerge at about this time, including 2 Scammel tractor lorries specially equipped to carry cable drums, and 2 AEC 4 tonne vehicles fitted out to carry poles up to 68 feet in length.

During World War 1 the POED had progressed from bicycles to motor cycles, but it was in 1919 that the first serious efforts were made to form a motor transport fleet, with the purchase of about 600 miscellaneous surplus army vehicles of all sizes up to 3 tonnes carrying capacity. Following that start, the need to tailor motor vehicles for the specialist engineering work associated with the public telecommunications services in the UK has been actively pursued continuously.

With the expansion in POED transport between the wars, making it one of Britain's largest fleets, a comprehensive maintenance system was set up to ensure the efficient running of the vehicles. This was backed by a budgeting system to ensure that sufficient funds were available in future years to expand and renew the fleet. The size of the emerging POED fleet was such that it was responsible in a large way for directing the efforts of the Motor Vehicle manufacturing industry for the eventual good of other concerns in the public and private sectors.

When I joined the POED in 1947, a good degree of standardisation of the fleets of specialised vehicles had occurred, even though the external gangs' Albions were being introduced gradually, as the variety of Morris Commercial vehicles which preceded them reached the end of their useful lives. Later in my apprenticeship, I came to regard the Morris 1000 as the standard small van for both the Line Maintenance and rural Exchange Construction occupations, but it was always a high point in any week when I was passenger in a Morris Y 10 cwt van, with its more powerful engine and wider range of facilities. The Technical Officers who were allocated these "Rolls Royces" of the fleet were privileged indeed.

On graduating out of my apprenticeship I was required to drive on my own account, and although already a holder of a full driving licence I had to pass another Driving Test with the POED's own Test Examiner. This proved to be much more stringent that the normal test, and included a hill start on Balkerne Hill, Colchester, with a match box placed behind my back wheel to indicate that I did not run backwards at all.

By 1978, the Business had developed into some 50 defined Engineering work occupations, most of which required mobility for their successful operation. These occupations were served by 20 main types of vehicle, with 53,000 vehicles operated by around 120,000 mobile engineering staff members. In 1971, I was transferred into the Motor Transport Utilisation Management post in the Eastern Region of what was then Post Office Telecommunications, as the old POED was phased out in favour of the new nationalised industry in 1968/9. This covered responsibility for the size and nature of the fleet of around 4,000 vehicles serving the needs of the 6 Telephone Areas of the Region. Having successfully rationalised the fleet in the next 6 years, it was in 1978 that I found myself working in central London on the utilisation of all 53,000 vehicles, reporting through a Head of Group to the Chief Motor Transport Officer, Jack Birks, to whom, as with Clifford Riley earlier, I owe much in regard to my managerial development in the Business.

Post Office engineering vehicles had largely become mobile workshops, or in the case of the small vans, mobile tool chests. The basic task of the vehicle was to get the Technician to his work site and then provide him with a base from which to work. The only full-time drivers in the Telecommuniations Business were stores drivers, some of whom were based in field localities, but most of whom were employed in the Supplies Dept which had developed from the old Stores Dept.

At the end of the 70s, as the Telecommunications network continued to grow and diversify, so did its motor transport fleet. This necessitated tight control over the number and type of additional and replacement vehicles provided. A considerable amount of effort was put in by myself and my colleagues in Motor Transport and the Data Processing Executive to introduce computer control over this situation, and we held the fleet growth to 3.5% compared with a 5.0% per annum network growth. This was a fascinating study, as the vehicle provision profiles for the different occupational group bandings were wholly dissimilar.

As the need to supplement the capital network diminished, so did the workforce employed on this type of work, the only complication being the ratio of direct labour work to contract.

Also, the maintenance transport needs related to the totality of the existing network, so the vehicle needs for maintenance, though large, were fairly stable.

However, Telephone Fitting and Installation work tended to fluctuate wildly, being governed largely by the national economic situation of the day and the whims of the customers. Even when the economy went into reverse a few years later, telephone cessation requests brought about a peak of work for the Fitters, but not the Installers who used a larger van.

Coincident with this statistical conundrum, I was called upon to leave my mark upon the evolution of the fleet by revising the interior layouts of the 7cwt and 15 cwt standard vans, necessitating co-operation with about a dozen specialist colleagues who were the national reference points for the Engineering works practices in 20 or so occupational groups. By this means I was able to introduce, nationwide, louvred panels and plastic bins in the 2 vehicle types, to match the new revisions of the tool and stores layouts for each occupation concerned. Each of these variants had to be "cleared" with the Post Office Engineering Union, both at national and branch levels. This was achieved for the Bedford HA 7cwt van and the 15cwt Dodge Spacevan in 1978 and 1979 respectively, just in time to change the manufacturers' specification for several thousand of each type ordered by PO Telecommunications.

One of the advantages of the new interior layouts was the neater and more methodical stowage of the kit of tools and stores, and in the case of the Maintenance Jointer it meant that he could get into the back of his van for the first time ever. We held the trial at 15 differing locations throughout the UK, one of which was Kingston-on-Thames in the London Region. Predictably, the National Executive members of the Union, based at Ealing, chose the Kingston vehicle for their field visit, as it was the nearest. I felt it prudent to pay the Jointer a visit before the Union people arrived, but with the London South-West Telephone Manager looking on, I was horrified to be confronted with a frightful mess of bins and jointing clutter all over the van floor. The Jointer was a tall and gangling man with a permanent smile. The Telephone Manager and I agreed privately that this had to be the premature end of the trial. The Union arrived, and with one look at the mess pronounced "Yuk!" My only defence was to carry on with my normal procedure, and started to give my standard questionnaire questions to the Jointer. How did he like the new layout ? "I think it's great !" The next question was "Why?" "Because it allows me to keep my van much tidier". Our minds all boggled as to what his previous layout was like, and the meeting dissolved in laughter which was incomprehensible to the Jointer. The trial was deemed a success and a new practice which was to last at least 15 more years became standard.

Another practical timetabling problem became apparent when a phone call from Scotland reminded me that the schools there break up for the Summer Holidays much earlier than in England, and the Bedford HA trials at Penicuik and Dalkeith would have to be advanced by a month, giving me less than a week to get 2 new kitted-out vehicles to Edinburgh. Our normal delivery method was to advise our contract delivery firm of the need, but the notice was too short. There was nothing else for it than to deliver them myself. I enquired of British Rail at Kings Cross what spaces there were on the Motorail, and found there was only one, which I accepted, and bent all kinds of rules to move the vehicle without an accompanying passenger. The only option I had was to drive the other van from London to Edinburgh in a day, the 21st of June 1978. The HA van was a highly practical and economic little vehicle but a significant number of the Technician drivers complained about backache, mainly because of the (ill-advised) existence of the Hillman Hunter Estate Car in the fleet for carrying expensive delicate equipment. Many were the hours I wasted turning down spurious requests for the Hillmans for more run-of-the-mill work. I drove the HA to Edinburgh, something approaching 400 miles, with no ill effects, and even called in at the Leeds office en route to fix their 1978/9 Transport budget. Next morning, at Edinburgh, I held a meeting to launch the trial, and asked for comments from the assembled Technicians. One man spoke up "Of course, the Bedford HA gives you backache if you drive it for any distance". I had only to tell him that I had driven his new van myself from London the previous day to strike the whole meeting dumb, and to launch another successful trial.

This Chapter would not be complete without mention of the Headquarters pool and dedicated car fleet for the use of the senior staff of the business, and that amazing group of men, the Chauffeurs. Although this fleet was modest in size by BT standards, the vehicles and their chauffeurs, and the booking system, took up a grossly disproportionate amount of the Vehicle Utilisation Section's time.

Having only recently arrived in Headquarters comparatively wide-eyed and innocent from the Field, I was lulled from my disillusionment by this happening. The Chauffeur to the Chairman, then Sir William Barlow, was forbidden to smoke in the limousine, as Sir William had a great aversion to the habit. One day the Chairman entered the car filled with a blue haze, and asked Fred why he was smoking. "Well, you see, sir, it's me nerves". "What have you to be nervous about ?" "Well, you see, sir, when I'm taking you to these important places, I'm really ashamed of this old uniform". Sir William looked hard at the 1 year-old uniform, and, although not entirely convinced, ordered the Utilisation Section to get him a new uniform. The Official Tailor, tape measure about his neck, arrived from the Materials Dept in Swindon, but when he started to measure Fred, the whole corps of Chauffeurs raised such a complaint that it was clear that they must all receive equal treatment. That night, Fred was the toast of the town. The same Fred, some time later, was driving the limousine along London Wall, when a battered old Morris Minor 1000 estate car drove over the red light and hit the Chairman's car amidships, causing no little damage. Fred, who had seen it all before, walked round to the Morris driver's window to find that the culprit was no less than a Mother Superior of Irish extraction driving 6 nuns to Mass. The lady protested "It was not my fault ! And if it was I would never admit it!"

At one stage I had responsibility for trialling alternative fuels for the propulsion of PO Telecoms & BT vehicles, but did not succeed in breaking away from the fume-producing Petrol and Diesel. The six 15 cwt electric vehicles I trialled at Stevenage were reasonably efficient until tachographs were fitted, inducing all sorts of interesting interactions between the vehicles' traction circuits and the auxilliary circuits, eg stopping dead when the right-hand flashing indicator was operated. Most of the PO Engineering depots also had insufficient electric mains current available to charge more than one or two vans overnight. The other trial, at Leeds, tried out Liquid Petroleum Gas (LPG), but no sooner had the technology been perfected than the Government claimed its "pound of flesh" by introducing a hydrocarbon tax on LPG, so killing the concept economically.

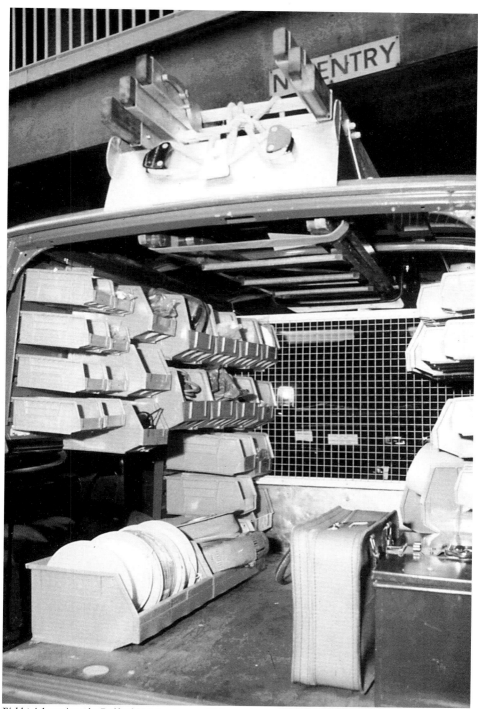

*Field trial version of a Bedford HA 7cwt van with louvred panels and plastic bins*

*Regional and Area Geographical Organisation*

# Chapter 5

# *The Organisation*

For as long as the public telegraph and telephone service has existed in Britain, as elsewhere, two fundamental questions have been almost continually addressed outside the Business as regards the way in which it is organised, ie, whether it should be publicly or privately owned, and whether control over the work should be centralised or decentralised.

Both these questions are imponderable, as different countries' administrations have arrived at opposite conclusions for the same service, eg, British Telecommunications plc is a private sector British company, whereas in Germany the service was until recently managed by Deutsche Bundespost, and more recently Deutsche Telekom. In the USA there is central private ownership of the trunk network, while some local networks are private and some are owned by local authorities.

Both the ownership and control systems have, up to now, alternated on slow-changing cycles, from one option to the other, reflecting both the political persuasion of the administration of the day, and the need for each new Chairman of the Business or functional Director to make his or her mark. At such levels the Centralisation/Decentralisation option gives ideal opportunity for real change without the embarrassment of internal or external criticism. During my 43 years with the business I witnessed 4 complete centralisation/decentralisation cycles. I supported them then, and still do now, not necessarily for the reason that the promulgator should be allowed to make his/her mark, but rather that a degree of change and uncertainty is generally a good way to keep a large organisation on its toes. My personal observation gives no indication that this beneficial motive was at the root of the cyclic changes which occurred.

The Ownership cycle is of much longer period, and so far only one-and-a-half cycles have occurred in just over 100 years. For the change from private to public ownership (eg, from the NTC to the PO) successive Liberal governments at the end of the 19th century chipped away at the matter and finally succeeded. The Labour government in the late 1960s set the scene for the split from the Post Office; later Labour governments saw the Business flourish as a Nationalised Industry; and, 5 years into the long Conservative reign from 1979, the Business became a plc, albeit constrained by quite stringent licence conditions.

Against the background of these macro changes, internal policy updates within the Business have proceeded on their own wave motions, the most notable of which is the alternation of periods in which the Accountants do or do not dominate the Business. It is good that they do so from time to time, but it is equally good that they have their lean spells as well, to keep Savings vs Service in proper balance, long-term. This situation was brought into sharp relief when, as Head of BT's Telephone Exchange Purchasing Section, I was told of an Inner London District's success in selling a £multi-million office automation scheme in the face of fierce competition. However, this would not work without the back-up of £4 million worth of new public exchange equipment to be supplied in 6 months, without prior knowledge for the current capital budget. The Headquarters Finance Dept's rule (which had been perpetuated from pre-privatisation days) was that all unbudgeted purchases over £1 million must be approved by the Capital Authorisation Committee. I made my case for authorisation of the urgent London purchase by correspondence, but the Committee Secretary, having consulted his Chairman, said he would put the item on the agenda for 2 months time, due to the high value of the case. Clearly, that would have lost the office automation job for London, so an expedient signature of the right level was obtained from the London Regional Director, so bypassing the Capital Authorisation Committee. So started a flow of correspondence on misappropriation of authority between the Capital Authorisation Committee and myself, but the order had been placed, and BT London was able to capitalise on its success. The same failure of the Headquarters executive functions to appreciate workface needs in the field was cited in the Bridgeman Report in 1932, 56 years earlier.

Another interesting subject in the context of BT's internal policy changes is the ever-increasing Devolution of Powers from Headquarters to the Field — during Decentralisation phases, that is. It is now not unknown for outward payments on national contracts, due to be paid from District offices, to be delayed beyond the contractual limit because that is expedient for the District's short-term cash flow, despite Headquarters' protestations to the contrary. District Boards also argue their macro-scene as justification for detailed changes to agreed budgets, although these are usually on a lesser scale than the office automation case quoted above.

So what changes to the organisational structure have happened against such a complex and changing policy backdrop ?

During the early 1930s, a large group of MPs recognised the potential of the Telephone, Telegraph and Postal Services, and strove to release them from the hide-bound Civil Service shackles which had governed the operations of the Post Office for nearly a century. Their pressure brought about the setting up of Lord Bridgeman's Committee in 1932 to study the current organisation and make recommendations for change.

Up to then, organisational progress from the original Post Office structure of the early century had been very slow to unfold. Fundamentally, the POED was backed administratively by the Accountant General's Dept (AGD), although the gentlemen of the AGD (there being no ladies there above the second or third tier of management) would argue that the AGD "controlled" the operations of the POED. It cannot be denied that all expenditure by the Engineers had to be authorised by the appropriate AGD Clerical level, although it is doubtful whether the authorisers understood many of the salient points in the cases made. Thus, many cases put for authorisation were subject to very long delays. These were the days of a Headquarters called the Engineer-in-Chief's Office (E-in-CO), a title dating back to the 1800s. There were Superintending Engineers, 1st and 2nd Class Engineers, Assistant Engineers, Chief Inspectors and Inspectors, all managing the work at their appropriate levels, and supervising the "rank & file" workforce of Skilled and Unskilled Workmen (ie no ladies at all). By 1912, the 2 classes of Engineer had become Executive Engineers. These grades worked either in the E-in-CO, working on the production of working practices in Engineering Instructions (EIs), or in Districts, in the field, doing the bidding of the E-in-CO.

The implementation of Bridgman was characteristically slow, and all that was done before World War 2 suspended it altogether was the replacement of the District Engineers' offices by 61 new Telephone Areas, under the control of Telephone Managers, a new concept with the one Manager in charge of Engineering, Clerical, Sales and Traffic Divisions. The year after the War ended, the next phase of Bridgman was the abolition of the Chief Inspector grade. Half these gentlemen were automatically promoted to Assistant Engineer, and the rest demoted to Inspector, a situation of tension which was at its height when I joined the service in 1947.

Numerically, the Engineering Division dominated in every Telephone Area. The much smaller Clerical Division dealt with the pay, telephone bills and the like, and the Chief Clerk of the Area co-ordinated the Budget and general financial matters. The Traffic Divisions in this post-war period had a thankless task to do, in trying to ensure that enough lines and equipment were provided at the right time to keep up with the increasing demand for service. All of which made the Sales Division something of a joke, with unstimulated demand outstripping supply almost everywhere, leaving the Sales staff to explain away to irate would-be customers why they could not be connected for 6 months. The big fallacy in this Area structure was the obvious need for the different Divisions to work together as teams, but their Civil Service-like vertical hierarchies tended to have the opposite effect, with many minor matters having to be resolved by correspondence "over the arch". But for all their faults, Telephone Areas were to last nearly 50 years, coinciding precisely with the 50 years of existence of the UAX exchanges in their service to the rural customers.

With the old AGD and E-in-CO now merged into a unified Headquarters structure, it was deemed necessary to set up a Regional intermediate functional tier, to reduce the number of budget negotiations with field. 10 such Regional offices were formed, and advantage was taken to concentrate in them such infrequently-occurring work as was not economic at Area level, eg the approval level for proposed new local and junction cable networks. Even less frequent functions were reserved to Headquarters, such as the planning of the expansion and modernisation of the Trunk Network. Although the Regional offices administered, on average, 6 Telephone Areas each, the Region covering my early career was a monster, the Home Counties Region, covering 12 Areas from the Wash to the South Coast. By 1968 the seemingly endless discussions on the size of Home Counties Region bore fruit with the split into the South-East and Eastern Regions, each with 6 Areas. My promotion to Executive Engineer brought me into the Eastern Region headquarters as one of its founder-members, back in Colchester.

But no matter what organisational structure is in vogue in the telephone service, the perennial question is always What To Do With London. The London Region was comprised of 11 Telephone Areas. Six of the London Areas had boundaries with the adjacent Provincial Areas, leaving an inner core of four, and a notional "Long Distance Area". The outer six were, in effect, "ordinary" Areas with a strong urban flavour. However, the inner four contained the national seat of Government, the City, and all the great institutions of the United Kingdom, and were thus unique.

All of which is very grand when compared with some of the Provincial situations in which Telephone Areas were small and geographically widespread, such as Scotland West. The size of Area determined the Telephone Managers' salaries, which were banded in descending order from Class 1 to Class 3. The Managers of the Class 3 Areas, such as Lincoln and Norwich, felt themselves as second class citizens, and sometimes tried to extend their responsibilities. Earlier I mentioned the Cambridge Area as being illogically long and thin, possibly because of the Royal Broadcasts from Sandringham. Without the King's Lynn control area, which contained Sandringham, the Cambridge Area would have been a much more normal Class 2 Area, and the Telephone Manager at Norwich wasted no time in pointing the anomaly out to the Home Counties Regional hierarchy, leading to a series of meetings on the matter. Clifford Riley, the Cambridge Area Engineer, accompanied his Manager at the meetings, and was quite prepared to sacrifice King's Lynn, due to its poor performance and low productivity. Norwich argued that whereas the Telephone Manager's Office at Cambridge was 44 miles and 400 yards from the King's Lynn office, the equivalent distance from Norwich was only 44 miles dead. Then started a catalogue of other public services at King's Lynn which were managed from Norwich, including Local Government services, Electricity, Gas, Water, Hospitals ..... By now, Clifford got restive and, thinking that Norwich "doth protest too much", interrupted to pose the question "Chairman, ask him which Bishop it comes under !" Rather taken aback, the Regional Director, who was chairing the meeting said "Very well, Mr Riley, which Bishop does it come under?" Realising now what he had started, Riley muttered "The Bishop of Thetford, and that's in the Cambridge Area". The meeting dissolved in laughter, and Cambridge kept King's Lynn, poor performance and all.

The network continued to grow and to provide more diverse facilities and services. Thus, second and even third Area Engineers began to appear in the larger Class 1 and 2 Areas, with, in some cases, a Deputy Telephone Manager to co-ordinate them. With the passage of time, Telephone Managers became General Managers, and everyone had to forget the familiar TMO in favour of

GMO. This formation survived the split from the Post Office in 1968/9, when the Post Office Telecommunications nationalised industry was born. The remarkable and ironic result of this was the setting up of completely separate Postal Regional Headquarters, at considerable cost. This was ironic because the Postal business, up to that time, had regularly made a loss per annum, which was conveniently subsidised by the profitable Telecommunications business. The Postal loss was now there for all to see, unclouded by the Telecom success. Sixteen years later, Postal had pulled itself up by its bootlaces and improved its financial position, which was fortunate as the telecommunications business, now called British Telecommunications, or British Telecom for short, became a plc, so eradicating any lingering doubt as to whether it might again one day subsidise the postal business. BT's new status in 1984 (coincident with Orwell's Brave New World) necessitated a change away from the Old Order, and scrapped 50 years' history of Telephone Areas in favour of Districts. There were only 30 District offices, so cutting the overhead costs of the 61 Area offices, thus pleasing the City pundits and the Shareholders. Then followed fairly frequent shuffling of the pack, reducing still further the number of Districts along the way. The Cambridge office, with its rich history, was a victim of this first District review, as the ever fortunate Colchester office took over the Anglia District. The Districts lasted between 5 and 6 years, after which they were succeeded by a new Zonal arrangement with even fewer offices controlling operations. As one who served in the POED in those far-off settled days, I see the present reducing period of existence of field organisation systems as reflecting Rudyard Kipling's Indian Tiger, who chased his tail faster and ever faster.

Meanwhile, something far more complex was happening in Headquarters. The last act of significance to come out of the Dollis Hill Research Station was the invention of Viewdata, in 1971, bringing news and information on to television screens, the brainchild of Sam Fedida. It had long been recognised that the job Dollis Hill had to do had outgrown the premises there, so soon after, in 1975, The Post Office Research Centre moved out to pastures new at Martlesham Heath, near Ipswich in Suffolk, to purpose-built laboratories and offices more worthy of the important job now emerging in the solid-state technology Telecommunications "explosion". At this stage, "blue sky" research was still very much the order of the day, reflecting the pre-nationalisation days when balance sheets were not kept within the business. For example, high technology tubes called Waveguides were very seriously considered for the next generation of multi-channel transmission of telephony and telegraphy by radio, but this development had to fall in favour of Microwave and satellite radio transmission, the burgeoning new idea of Pulse Code Modulation, and later Optical Fibre Cables.

Every week an impressive list of patent applications appeared in the house magazine, touching every aspect of telecommunications engineering. This continued well into the 80s, when the introduction of Total Quality Management created the requirement of a cascaded Mission to be written for every segment of the business. Inevitably, in the pre-privatisation period, every Director and his management team asked themselves why they were there, what the real objectives of their part of the business were, and what their future roles should

71

be. The financial pressures of private ownership sharpened awareness of where else research and development could be done, so a gradual shift of emphasis towards Customer Apparatus and Services, and away from the general network and switching aspects began, and is still happening into the 90s. This same philosophy was applied across the whole of Headquarters, inevitably leading to frequent reorganisations within and between Departments. With reducing staff numbers, devolved responsibilities increased, and the period from 1985 to 1990 saw much change and even instability in the Headquarters Departments, with only broad guidelines from the Board. Not until after this period did the centrally-driven economy measures really start in earnest.

# Chapter 6

# *Accounts and Accountability*

Right up to 1969, the Post Office, including its Engineering Dept., was a Department of the Civil Service. As in all other Civil Service Departments, no direct Balance Sheet was kept, and we who worked in the POED, and tried to manage it, had no idea whether we were making a profit or a loss.

On my first day of employment with the POED in 1947, I was asked by letter to report to Mr A.G. Hamilton at All Saints' House, Colchester, at 7.30 am. My parents were a bit surprised by the early starting hour, but insisted that I wore my best suit to make a good initial impression. I found All Saints' House a hive of activity, with dozens of overalled grease-covered men milling about. When I plucked up courage to ask for Mr Hamilton, one of the men said "Oh, you mean Titch!" and directed me to a door marked Foremen. In the smaller room beyond the door I found 6 more men with greasy overalls, but this time they were all sitting down filling in forms in a blue cigarette haze. By instinct I went up to the smaller man and introduced myself. "So you're the new boy! How did you know I was Mr Hamilton?" So began my 43-year career with a faux pas, but at the same time I was made immediately aware of the importance of the completion of a Time Sheet for every man, for pay purposes, and an Allocation Sheet or Progress Report so that the amount of time on every defined work type could be logged.

It seems strange in hindsight that employees' time should be logged so assiduously while so little attention was given to the size and nature of the workforce. This thunderous point came home to me hard when, 10 years later, I found myself Area Training Officer at Cambridge, with an Area Engineer and 4 voracious Executive Engineers expecting to be supplied with excellent staff, trained efficiently on the right disciplines, at exactly the right moment in precisely the right part of the Area. I was never more conscious of the creaking of the Civil Service rigid system as I was then. In my 11 years in that post, I recruited, trained and placed 500 out of the Area's 1,500 engineering staff. Each of these men had to serve a 3-year probationary period, after which they became "established" Civil Servants, which made them almost non-dismissable. While the people of the Clerical Division were busying themselves with pyramids of paper based on analysis of the Allocation Sheets, I felt an awesome personal responsibility to make absolutely certain that everyone recruited was a worthy new member of the business, and would not turn into a 44-year liability. From a

Civil Service point of view, this check was for past jail records and poor health, but my net as trainer had to be cast much deeper, covering job performance and ability to get on with colleagues and the public. This sense of responsibility became even more awesome if one stopped to think for a moment that at that time 95% of POED managers were recruited at a lower level for their technical ability, and not at all for their managerial ability. This was, perhaps the biggest loophole in the Civil Service system, as the Establishment scheme led to overwhelming promotion in-house, and then only rarely cross-discipline.

Every "Major Work" which increased the size of the cable and overhead networks had to have financial estimates authorised at defined levels, in advance. These estimates were carried out in great detail, following detailed field surveys, all finely documented for the eventual working instructions for the job. Internal (Indoor) and External (Outdoor) Planning Groups existed in all Telephone Areas to do the Surveys and Estimating. Many of the jobs were elbowed out of the Works Programme because of the finite allocation of funds to the Area from Headquarters via the Region, so the Area and Regional Boards had to exercise the wisdom of Solomon as to which schemes went ahead, and which had to wait or be cancelled. I remember being horrified at the 110% overheads added to every job, to cover the general running costs of the Department on a fully-allocated basis.

The Current Account covering Telephone Installation and Maintenance was managed differently, on outturn measurement and sales forecasts.

Only rough data were available to senior management to judge the value for money expended on the work. In cable network planning for example, a Spare Pair Return gave the overall picture of how much unused cable there was in the ground, but said nothing about the situation in particular streets or villages where flag cases were likely to develop. Then there was the Exchange Inventory and Work Unit check, an incredibly complex invention by clerks in Headquarters who paid no regard to the hours and hours of work needed to complete them, update them, and finally use them. Clifford Riley gave me an extra-mural job at Cambridge to analyse how many Work Units each Maintenance Technical Officer was holding down in his own small domain. I went running to Riley when I found that one man had 950 Work Units, whereas another only had 250. The Area Engineer was quite unperturbed, and accepted the imbalance, because he knew the capabilities of the 2 men concerned. The only difference, he said, was that the more efficient man would one day be Area Engineer, and the other would be stretched to remain a Technical Officer.

By contrast, revenue received in the Area office was something completely apart. This was the domain entirely of the Clerical Division, who sent out the bills and manned the front office. In Engineering terms, the great crime was to generate a Departure from Estimate on a planned job. How much revenue that job would generate was never known under the Civil Service system. The net result of this was (and still is in the present Civil Service) a Management striving to do well with their specialised estimates and outturn stewardship, but having to strive still harder to get any of the work put into the Programme for actually doing. The "Clerical" people who assembled the Works Programmes and the senior staff who approved them were often guilty of relying upon the "wisdom of Solomon" rather than going into the real merits of proposed schemes with the initiators. Often, "Stop-Go" on the Capital Account was matched by "Go-Stop" on the Current Account, and vice versa.

It took some time for this system to die, and it continued to irritate well into the nationalised period. When, in 1974, the Middle East oil suppliers caused ripples in all Western economies, an across-the-board budget cut of 12% was imposed from PO Telecommunications Headquarters, just before the start of the final quarter of the Financial Year. I was carefully monitoring the delivery of new small mechanical aids (roadbreakers, small excavators and the like) to the Eastern Region, when I was told by the Regional Budget Officer that the rest of the Mechanical Aids Budget had to be "cut". I protested that we had contractual obligations to the suppliers, and was curtly told to break the contract and pay the resultant penalties "next year". I was so upset by the illogic of this instant "solution" that I discussed the matter with the Head of the Headquarters Group dealing with Mechanical Aids provision. He was equally incensed, so we resolved to pay a visit to the mandarin in London who, as we saw it, started the problem. After much trying we managed to get a slot in his busy programme, and we were ushered into a large oak- panelled room in Armour House. "Does the case have more than £1,000,000 significance ?" "No, it's only £600,000". "Then I am not interested." My colleague erupted, causing our protagonist to go on to an entirely different tack. "Who are you dealing with in Eastern Region ?" We told him, and he bade us goodbye, to go on with his important life. Gloomily we left, bewailing our failure, but when I got back to Colchester I reported my lack of success to the Budget Officer. "Lack of success in what ?" he asked. "The 12% cut in the Mechanical Aids budget." "What 12% cut ?" We had won.

But gradually the new Nationalised Industry began to balance Income against Expenditure. Cost Ratios, measuring current and capital expenditure against each £ of income, became all the rage for a period in Management Accounting statistics, but faded later in significance when it was realised that cascaded functional breakdowns in this form were of little practical use. The old Engineering and Traffic management statistics which, prophetically, had started in the Civil Service days, gave quite a good indication of the average time to repair a fault or to answer a Directory Enquiry call, but did not give the costs of these services. More complex statistics were invented, such as the Motor Transport Capital Indicator, and the rapidly growing use of computers allowed for otherwise complex calculations to be done routinely.

Then came the inevitable, as cost awareness was generated by the Board's strong desire to present annual improvements in the Report & Accounts Balance Sheet by this, the flagship of Nationalised Industries which, apart from the occasional small abberation, left all the others standing. An experimental group of Telephone Areas became Profit Centres, in the same way that retail shops strive to be profitable. While this gave Area General Managers the degree of self-motivation and autonomy they had always been seeking, it was plain to many of us from the start that the far-flung rural Areas (eg, Scotland West, which did not include Glasgow) would never make a profit as their Overheads were high and their Income low. Statute also demanded (as it still does) that telephone service be supplied wherever demanded. Profit targets, therefore, had to take account of a "normal" trading position of each Area, be it one of profit or loss, so that an improving annual trend could be recognised (or, indeed, any trend). Much more ambitious profit targets were applied to the large urban Areas, who were thus not allowed to bask in their favoured positions.

As always, Headquarters was more complex and difficult. In what appeared a very short time, all Headquarters' units were declared Profit Centres, Cost Recovery Centres or Overheads. The Profit Centres were given profit targets like the larger Areas; the Cost Recovery Centres necessitated the introduction of inter-unit notional charging; and the Overheads were somewhat uncomfortable units in which to work (such as the non-project part of Management Services Dept). Overheads units were thereafter always the first parts of the business to be phased out or pruned during economy drives.

Of these categories, the Cost Recovery Centres were by far the more interesting, and quite complex inter-unit charging arrangements with high attendant compiling and processing costs were set up to handle the "Funny Money". It was not uncommon, in Management Services project work, to be meeting the needs of an internal Engineering "customer" Section in, say, BT International, and arguing with the same unit's Accountant over justifying a transfer charge of, say, £25, for a small part of the work. Much later, after Privatisation, the folly of all this was realised and a more streamlined system was evolved.

The whole scene is really so complex as to pose imponderable questions to any Telephone Service administration. For example, properly managed Network Maintenance is undeniably a necessary cost, but it does not generate any income by itself. The income from the much smaller Installation function must always subsidise Maintenance.

While on the subject of Maintenance, the value lost to the network operator as a result of the severance of a trunk or junction link has always been a fascinating study. A typical scene, sadly all too familiar, is a roadworks site at which mechanical diggers are operating, one of which accidentally slices through a telecommunications cable. Such cables can carry 10,000 or more voice or data channels, but BT and its predecessors have always been unsuccessful in claiming compensation for the value of calls lost, pending restoration. This is significant in many cases and can amount to £1,000 or more per minute. The Courts argue that nobody can prove how many of the lost calls are re-made by the customers after the link has been restored, and the usual judgement is to award compensation only for the physical repair costs of the broken cable, which is small by comparison. I was told once that when an inshore fisherman trawled up a submarine cable to the Netherlands, off the Suffolk coast, the Lowestoft magistrates awarded lost call time compensation to Post Office Telecommunications, but an Appeal Court overturned this judgement, which would have been a very expensive precedent for all those who damage public utility plant.

I cannot end this Chapter without mentioning personal, as well as corporate, accountability. During the Nationalised stage, Management by Objectives was introduced for all Managers of Level 3 and above. This coincided with the introduction of the concept that people in these ranks were "above" specialisms, on promotion. Each year, coincident with the Annual Appraisal one-to-one interview between the senior manager and his/her superior, about 5 Personal Objectives were agreed for the coming year, for review and assessment at next year's counselling. This, of course, is a good idea only if the Objectives are challenging enough, so the system was widely open to abuse. Later, since Privatisation, the scheme has been extended down to lower ranks.

Generally, during the long evolution of the business, financial responsibilities per rank or grade have increased, no doubt due to the rate of expansion since the early days. Thus, while accountability to one's seniors is always important, the ultimate accountability is to oneself and one's conscience, whether in a great public business, a private company, or anywhere else.

# Chapter 7

# *Efficiency Projects*

I can imagine many readers flying straight to this Chapter as a humorous diversion, in view of the national political pastime of denigrating the British public telephone service. Even some of the younger BT employees of my acquaintance are depressed by being associated with such an allegedly inefficient business.

Under such circumstances the paradoxical truth is that an Efficiency specialist, trained to be both questioning and objective, is in a better position to judge the reality internally than is an external political observer whose motivation has no connection at all with the business or the quality of service achieved. This was underlined when, after much taunting by the Government of the day when requiring the newly-privatised BT to go into competition with other companies, BT acquitted itself so well without undue adjustment that the competitors raised complaints to the Office of Telecommunications (OFTEL) about the unfairness of BT's network knowledge, infrastructure and experience.

This good, efficient operational base did not happen overnight on Privatisation Vesting Day, but was the product of much assiduous effort at Headquarters and Field levels since World War 2. Unfortunately, the scale of the operation and the difficult working circumstances in London and the other large cities have often brought less favourable results over the years than I experienced personally in the Provinces. It is no surprise that Government and the large national institutions judge the whole network's performance by what they see in the capital, but this is no different to the problems of public telecommunications in every principal city in the World. It does not take much imagination to realise that someone receiving Technician's pay for working in the centre of a big city such as London must suffer the same high costs and rush-hour transport privations as his more senior colleagues, so he must possess much self-motivation to do as well as his provincial peers. Incidentally, two-thirds of the UK network exists outside London.

Efficiency project work in the Engineering field has gone on in the "back room" of the business continuously since the late 1940s, resulting in many improved methods and practices, bringing impressive results and cost savings. I can quote only a few examples here, all of which relate to improvements in the routine everyday tasks of the business, rather than brilliant new concepts which also emerged regularly from Dollis Hill and Martlesham Heath. Another reason why these good ideas are not appreciated by the end-customer (and the politicians) is the fact that only some of them relate to Customer Installation and Service, the rest being points of good housekeeping which could apply to any forward-looking business.

Surprisingly (or maybe not, since he was Irish), it was Oscar Wilde who said that "Man was not made for disturbing dirt; that sort of work should be done by a machine". The same thought occupied the minds of the Mechanical Aids Development Branch at Carlton House, Wembley, in the early 1960s, with the overhead and underground gangs in mind; not for the same altruistic reasons as Wilde's thoughts, but simply to speed the work and to improve productivity at the expense of a degree of outlay on machinery. The engineers at Wembley co-operated with manufacturers to arrive at the resultant Pole Erection Units now familiar at the roadside, and various types of Mechanical Digger.

Even more subtle developments were also in progress nationally in the late 1970s in the mainstream Motor Transport utilisation field, for which I was personally responsible. New standard vehicles from 7 cwts to 4 tonnes carrying capacity were brought into the 4,000-strong Eastern Region fleet either as Additionals, due to expansion of the business, or as Replacements due to the life-expiry of the old vehicles. Replacements outnumbered Additionals tenfold, and were justified only on the basis of the replaced vehicle's condition. With the close co-operation of the business's Data Processing Executive I put on to computer the vehicle fleet by number and type, and the staff by occupation, plus information on the normal size of working party and vehicle type for each occupation. Thus, the optimum fleet size by number and type for each Engineering Depot, and thence for each Area and Region, were calculated in an instant. In the first year of operation we removed 172 vehicles (of average value about £8,000 each) from the fleet by cutting the Replacement programme (hitherto unheard of) and rearranging the use of the rest of the fleet. As a side benefit the Engineering Staff Tree was automatically committed to computer to the greater benefit of Personnel and the preparers of the Manpower Budget. Thus heartened, I soon found myself in a Central London office of Headquarters, doing likewise to the national fleet of 53,000 vehicles. Not satisfied with this scheme alone, I also found myself, as mentioned previously, designing and trialling throughout the UK new radically-changed racking and plastic bins in the dominant 7 cwt and 15 cwt vehicles, and thus, in co-operation with all the Headquarters occupational specialists, incorporated a series of standard tool and stores layouts for all the occupational groups using these vehicles which were, and still are, effectively mobile tool boxes.

Another efficiency project I and my colleagues progressed in Headquarters was an automatic fault diagnosis computer scheme at the high call value Trunk Transit exchanges, replacing a teleprinter printout in unintelligible code. As mentioned earlier, this improved call attempt failures from 8% to only 2%, while breaking fraud attempts on international calls in the bargain.

As my last example I cite the case of Telephone Exchange equipment racks which, prior to digitisation, measured 10'6" by 4'6" by a few inches wide, and weighed up to about a tonne. They were much too long for trolley-loading on to the industry-standard mechanised tail-lift of standard stores-carrying vehicles, and so had to be man-handled into the lorries, presenting a real danger to those concerned in the operation, not to mention the risk of damage to the very valuable equipment. A locally-designed turntable-clamp device was the eventual answer, which helped not only PO Telecommunications but also the rack manufacturers for several years before the digitised equipment practices were introduced. These were smaller, lighter, and easier to handle.

Many such good ideas started in the minds of POED and BT staff all over the country who wished to improve the way in which they and their colleagues worked. The POED introduced a scheme of Awards for Suggestions, which obliged Headquarters' specialists to assess ideas from the Field, the best of which attracted monetary awards for the initiators, and publicity in the house magazine. The detail of the scheme has changed from time to time, a periodic face-lift which is always a good thing. The scheme, in essence, still exists in BT.

In the mid and late 1980s, the new science of Total Quality Management arrived in BT, as it did throughout most major companies. This organised Good Ideas as never before, set up formal Quality Teams, and registered Improvement Projects, as several methods of approach permeated into the UK from the USA. BT studied closely the doctrine of Deming's statistical control methods, refining and improving the statistics which originated back in the POED days; the "let's always put the Customer first" message from Tom Peters and Crosby; and Juran's voluminous works on the subject. These differing emphases threw up numerous questions — very important questions because the large scale of BT's operation (240,000 employees at the end of the 1980s) meant that all errors of strategy would be gross errors. Is the Customer always right ? Does he/she really know what is best for him/her in the high-tech environment of the 80s and 90s ? Who is the Customer, anyway ? (This question is of particular relevance to the Back Room Boys in the Cost Recovery type of unit).

The sudden sophistication of the Efficiency and Ideas "industry" has, since about 1988, brought radical, strategic changes of thinking within BT. One of the best features is the requirement for the Company and each Department to issue a Mission Statement pinpointing why it is there, as a starting point for the re-casting of its whole operation, its staffing profile, and the way in which the job is done. Once these decisions have been made, they are fully documented under British Standard BS 5750, and reviewed frequently. Such sophistication makes me wonder how we managed so well before. Perhaps it all comes down to real conscientiousness and real loyalty to the organisation.

# Chapter 8

# *The Unions*

The staff of the POED were represented by a quite bewildering array of Unions, but in true Civil Service fashion, none of them could really be described as militant. These continued into the Nationalised era, but when Privatisation was first seriously considered as a concept, the number of Unions was reduced down to a powerful few. Still, however, the Industrial Relations scene in the business could hardly be regarded as other than generally tranquil when compared with other large employers' businesses.

In the Civil Service days of the POED, an appropriate Whitley Council produced results which represented a good, balanced picture between the employer and the employed. As mentioned right at the beginning, pride of belonging to the POED was everything, and the employer was trusted 100% to agree a good deal with the staff. "Industrial Action" was unknown in the business.

Locally, in the Areas, the activities of the Post Office Engineering Union were confined to such local matters as leaking radiators at the Engineering Depot and changes to Repeater Station shiftwork rotas. My old Area Engineer at Cambridge had an infallible formula for keeping the peace with the Union. Once a month he and the Telephone Manager would invite the Chairman, Secretary and Treasurer of each of the 4 Union Branches in the Area to a general meeting to discuss their potential complaints. Clifford would call for "Any Complaints" from the floor, which led to one view from a Branch being denied or opposed by another Branch. The whole meeting then turned into a debate between the Union representatives for the whole of the hour dedicated to the meeting, during which Clifford did not utter another word. As for the Telephone Manager, he did not say anything at all. At the end, nothing was resolved, but everyone from the Union felt happy to have had their say. This procedure happened monthly for many years, and I was always amazed, when paying work visits to the field, to hear the Union officials praising the Telephone Manager for his good, skilful chairmanship.

Another Engineering Union was the Society of Telecommunications Engineers (STE), which was a sort of Managers' Club for the local bosses. Whenever anything remotely like a dispute with the POED appeared on the horizon, all the STE members felt acutely embarrassed, and had to carry out the difficult role of representing their own case as staff members while representing the Official case to the POEU members in the lower grades. Again, Clifford Riley was to the fore in his dealings with the STE. In 1947, when the Chief Inspector grade was abolished, the current post holders in that grade were regraded, some up to Assistant Engineer, and some down to Inspector. The deal was agreed nationally, giving STE Branch officers access to the regrading lists before the names were announced. My colleague Ray Stubbs, the Cambridge STE Chairman, knocked nervously on Mr Riley's door. Riley told Ray that he knew why he had come, and handed over the lists. Heartened, Ray noticed Riley putting on his coat, and asked if he would stay to discuss the lists. "No", said the Engineer. "I'm going home. You'll find the rest of my work in the in-tray." With that he left.

Being by far the youngest STE member at Cambridge in 1958 (at the tender age of 26) I felt greatly honoured to be asked to be Secretary of the Branch. However, I soon learned the catch which had put everyone else off this honorary job. Around a third of the Members in this typical Class 2 Area were aged between 60 and 65, products of the slow and easy promotion procedure of the Civil Service. Everybody's career details were unique, so innumerable queries on their pensions arose daily, not to mention "Death Benefits". Being already occupied 100% each day on the needs of the Area job, all these cases had to be addressed in the evenings. When my young family came along 5 years later, I was lucky to find another aspiring young member who was prepared to accept the honour, and take it on!

Paradoxically, it was only 10 years later when I found myself sitting on the Management Side of the Eastern Region Joint Council of Post Office Unions (COPOU for short). My own career development in the Regional office had brought me into the field of Efficiency, Productivity and Changes of Practice, so my particular responsibility on this august Committee was New Practices and the Code for Changes of Practice. A member of the Regional Board (a Controller) was Chairman, and a long-standing Branch Secretary of the POEU was Joint Chairman. Both sides agreed an Agenda a couple of days before each monthly meeting, and the Management and Staff sides confronted each other across the boardroom table. I remember well a couple of occasions when, right at the start of the meeting, the Staff Side Joint Chairman said "I would like to put the Agenda to one side, because it has come to my notice that one of my members has been victimised". He represented in total about 10,000 junior Engineering staff, so I was not really surprised that at least one of them thought he was being "victimised" at any given moment. I welcomed these diversions, because all the other possibly controversial items on the Agenda for which I was responsible went through "on the nod", because the "victimisation" allegations always took up the whole meeting. The Management were always totally unprepared for these instances, and could thus do nothing other than listen to all the detail for an hour or so, and then say they would look into it. Oddly, the reporting back on these cases at the next meeting never took more than a minute or two. As with the Cambridge union meetings with Riley, the Staff Side seemed mainly content to have "had their say".

During this period around 1973, a National Code for Engineering Changes of Practice was agreed with National COPOU and published as a Telecom

Instruction (TI). This formed something of a blank canvas on which the Regions could paint their own picture, and I was commissioned to produce the Draft Regional TI on Changes of Practice. The Staff Side, obviously, wanted as much flexibility in the Instruction as possible, but I knew there were a couple of "hawks" amongst the Regional managers who would have to put the new Code into practice. I drafted the document as objectively as I could, and circulated it to the Management for comment. At once, the "hawks" pronounced it too soft, and composed additional paragraphs placing stringent conditions on the Staff Side. I put them in, like a red rag to the Staff Side bull, where they were unceremoniously deleted. At the Regional COPOU, the Staff Side were content to have made their deletions, but nobody knows until now that it was only the "hawks'" additions which were cut out. These experiences prepared me very well for the later head-to-head negotiations I held with the POEU National Executive members when introducing new equipment and practices for national use. For a start, I knew the Change of Practice Codes inside out, and had learned the precious message that the Unions react worst when they are ignored, when they can cause embarrassing delays to new schemes. At Headquarters I found a good many senior folk who were even more hawkish than some of my old Regional colleagues, especially after the change of Government in 1979. These people would rather have implementation delayed than to speak first with the Unions, which appeared to me as time-wasting and counter-productive. When approached at the right time and in the right way, I always found the Unions nationally co-operative and quite forward-looking. I always found it useful to give them two choices as to method, knowing one to be a non-starter. They always chose the right option. When "selling" the POEU the concept of new-type racks and bins in small vans, I was able to conclude a deal with them by accepting the reinstatement of a parcel tray in the vehicle costing £7 per van. This reduced the whole-scheme savings from £200 to £193 per vehicle, which I then had to "sell" to the Chief Motor Transport Officer — a much tougher job than dealing with the Union! The POEU eventually became the new National Communications Union, when Privatisation was imminent.

Earlier I mentioned that I had to computerise the Area Engineering Staff Tree. As that also comprised a national Change of Practice, I found myself "dealing" with the Assistant General Secretary of the Civil & Public Servants Association (CPSA) which grew out of the old Civil Service Clerical Association, post-Nationalisation. Generally, his union was more militant at Branch level than was the POEU, and in 1978 they were in near panic over the introduction of Computers, which they saw as the precursors to job shedding. It took me quite a time to convince both the National Executive and the Branches that to commit the Staff Tree to computer would be beneficial to everyone. Again, polite consultation and explanation was the key to a successful outcome.

When, earlier, I was in charge of Mechanical Aids policy at Regional level, I was heavily involved in the aftermath of Accidents on Duty, and in such cases the Unions took upon themselves the responsibility for getting as much compensation for the aggrieved people as possible. The odd thing was that, as an "expert witness" my opinion was often asked both by the Union and the

Management on the same points.

On a different level above all this, the array of different Unions represented their members in the annual round of Pay Bargaining. I was never involved in this directly, but carefully watched the POEU negotiation, which always happened first, as an indicator of the likely STE settlement which always looked to the percentage agreed by the POEU as a precedent. (Both sides always said this was not so, but the results were always very consistent).

Lastly, the Unions represented their individual Members in disciplinary hearings, appeals against non-promotion and the like. The Union representative could attend the hearings to advise the Member, if he/she requested it, to advise on the spot. At the Nationalisation stage, in common with other large companies at the time, certain Union representatives were given seats on the Board, but this was discontinued later by mutual agreement.

# Chapter 9

# *Computers*

Analogue (ie, non-Digital) computers have existed for many years in various forms, but they were mainly academic curiosities with little commercial application.

The great revolution in computer technology took place from 1975 to 1985. Not only was business life, including BT's operations, changed dramatically by this development, but the 10-year period was itself evolutionary, making application strategy short-lived, and therefore expensive, if not confused.

As soon as solid state chip-based technology opened up all the commercial possibilities in the early 1970s, monstrous slow-acting "mainframe" digital computers came on to the scene in large businesses such as BT, usually with enough spare capacity via input "ports" to allow hired "time sharing" use by other Departments and smaller companies and organisations. At the start, most of the work was processed by Batch Input, and armies of operators produced Punched Cards from strictly regimented input data forms, to arrive at results of large routine processes. One such operation was the control of Stores Issues in PO Telecoms, in conjunction with the Vocabulary of Engineering Stores (Rate Book). Soon it was recognised that sub-programmes could be written to produce Owings Lists, and even to trigger re-order levels to avoid "stockouts" or over-stocking. Stores locations were also recorded, although the concept of Logistics control was not formalised until some 20 years later. Each requisition passing through Area offices was logged on a manual input to this scheme, which was known as Engineering Stores Control & Pricing (ESCAP). PO Telecoms' Data Processing Service (DPS) was at the forefront in these early days, offering a superb advisory service to all Departments on what was best for their schemes. The only unusual fact about the DPS was that they existed in the downbeat Commercial Road, between 2 kosher butchers ! (Maybe that was to discourage too many personal visitors like me ).

Being a public telephone authority, PO Telecoms was quick to realise that Voice Frequency Telegraphy (VF), used for some time for the slow transmission of data between Teleprinters on a special Telex switching network, merely needed speeding up to allow computers to "talk" to each other in Binary Code. Gradually the technique killed off a good proportion of Batch Input, in favour of remote dial-up to dedicated computer input-port lines. Immediately, sales reps carried small business briefcases in which ordinary telephone receivers could be enclosed, and sales data was sent from a small keyboard. This stage had been reached when, around 1976, I co-operated with my old friend John Leach at the DPS in Commercial Road on the computerisation of Vehicle and Staff records for the 6 Areas of the Eastern Region. The dial-up input from each Area office worked reasonably well on PO Telecom's IBM mainframe at Harmondsworth, but many people were frustrated when the monstrous machine was taken out of service for maintenance every evening at 5.30 pm. Users also had to rely on the staff at Harmondsworth to take "back-up" copies of all data stored, to guard against losing the results of all the input labour in the event of a "crash" of the machine, which was fairly frequent. When the Civil & Public Servants' Association (CPSA) held a strike in 1978, the Harmondsworth IBM was switched off, so testing the back-up service to the full, with variable results. One reason for the strike was a fear of job losses as computers took over a number of manual tasks, but the real benefit of computerisation, for me, was to make the machine produce, in an instant, useful data which would be impossible to produce manually, so giving greater management control. I have striven to achieve this in all schemes in which I have been subsequently involved.

The inflexibility of mainframe computers, their size and high costs, and thus the high cost of time-sharing, led the ever-resourceful Industry to go for the development of function-specific Microcomputers. These flooded the market in about 1980, and their price of £1,000 or less brought them well within Departmental financial limits, and they sprang up like mushrooms throughout PO Telecoms. Harmondsworth and the other mainframes lost their timeshare customers, and were left with the hardcore of non-urgent Batch Input work such as Statistics generation, ie, Micros took over on-line working, leaving off-line to the mainframes. It was realised, after about a year of this rapid change, that PO Telecoms' computing costs, now fragmented, were rocketing, and attempts were made to bolt the stable door rather late, by bringing in a Microcomputer authorisation scheme.

It was at this stage that I took over the Transit Exchange maintenance project on a sophisticated Alpha Micro computer at the Cambridge Trunk unit. This was typical of a scheme requiring a more "powerful" Micro than the authorising people were normally prepared to pay for, so I had to produce numerous Costings and Reports to justify the £3,500 expenditure, which eventually led to £millions saved.

Concern over the proliferation of Micros led to a policy, heavily involving the Data Processing Executive (DPE) which succeeded the DPS (but still adjacent to the kosher butchers !) to time-share locally on Minicomputers, which absorbed the work of a dozen or so Micros, gave inter-disciplinary data transfer and use, and gave a degree of central control. Typical of these was the Customer Services System (CSS), integrating Sales and Installation data, on-line.

Soon after, all BT middle and senior managers were encouraged to have their own small Micros, networked within the Department to a central Mini, via a Local Area Network, which is, perhaps, the scheme giving ultimate management control.

Something of a brake was put on all this by the Data Protection Act in the mid-1980s, requiring all computer schemes referring to people by name, to be centrally registered, and made available to the individuals concerned on request.

Having gained this experience I found myself, in the 1980s, carrying out recruitment interviews for the temporary appointment in all Headquarters Departments of Computer Sciences Sandwich Course undergraduates, and recommending appointments, as an extra-mural duty. This led to a special relationship between BT and the Computing Sciences Department at the City University, with whom I placed and judged a final year degree project for the development of a Management Game in conjunction with the British Institute of Management (now the Institute of Management).

*A BT Engineer working on a System X equipment panel*

*A Thorn-Ericsson Installation Engineer wiring-in BT International's
first Digital Exchange at Keybridge House, London*

# NATIONAL DIGITAL NETWORK

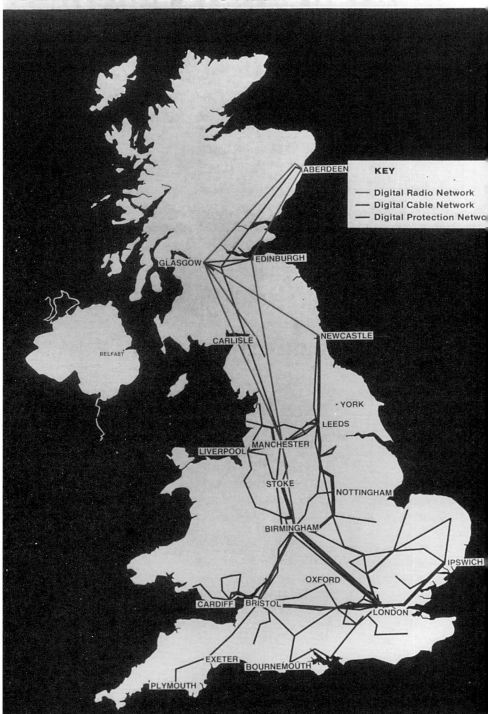

*The National Digital Network in the mid-1980s*

*BT Engineers working on the Processor Test Unit at Keybridge House Digital Exchange, 1984*

# Chapter 10

# *Digitisation*

As early as 1965, I attended an Institution of PO Electrical Engineers lecture at Cambridge, given by a gentleman named Duerdoth, on the use of the new Pulse Code Modulation (PCM) technique of transmission over junction lines, for a revolutionary new call switching facility. Under PCM, the transmitted speech is sampled, binary coded, transmitted as code, and then decoded at the other end. Mid-route "repeating" of the coded signals is much simpler than amplifying an actual speech signal, because each "pulse" is represented by Current On or Current Off. The use of this principle to replace the Strowger switching system on which my teeth had been cut represented, undoubtedly, the greatest quantum leap since telecommunications began. Of even greater importance is the fact that Computer data input lines and networking links can be switched without making any distinction with voice circuits.

With its customary caution and desire for 110% excellence from the outset, the PO Telecoms Research and Development Departments set up a joint venture with GEC, Plessey and STC to create a new Digital Switch for the British network, known as System X. Initially there were high hopes for the system as a world-beating export item, but the old POED track record of slow, cautious development opened the door to companies like Ericsson to conquer the World. When BT placed its contract for AXE10 digital switches in 1986, Ericsson had made sales to 72 other countries, while BT still only had hopes for System X abroad.

The key to Ericssons' success was the fact that they did not start from scratch, but adapted their AKE analogue stored programme control system to become the AXE digital system. BT also had Analogue Stored Programme Control switches in use, notably STC's large TXE4, but merely regarded these as stop-gaps between Strowger and the Digital era. The smaller TXE2 exchanges were provided by GEC and Plessey. Another short-lived family of analogue exchanges provided after Strowger in the British network was the Crossbar range of switches, provided for the Local Network by GEC and Plessey, and for the Trunk Network by STC. These Crossbar switches were really "accidents in time", because they represented the ultimate in electromechanical switching, far more reliable, fast and cheap to run than Strowger, but almost out-of-date by the time they were installed.

The development programme for System X was based on a great hierarchy of committees, each dovetailing into the overall strategic plan. The problem was that the "new generation" of Engineers recruited to develop the system were versed only in Digital technology, so once again Management Services were called in on an agency basis to plan the integration of the new system into the pre-existing analogue network, to be trialled at the first-ever System X exchange at Woodbridge, Suffolk, near the Martlesham Heath Research Station. In keeping with their illustrious POED forebears, Martlesham, the PO Telecoms Development Divisions, GEC, Plessey and STC saw the first target opening date for Woodbridge at the end of 1979 pass, then the next at the end of 1980. It finally opened in 1981. My part in all this was twofold. First, I had to re-write all the Technical Instructions (TIs) on all the routine operations carried out by an exchange Technical Officer. For example, when a new customer's line had to be connected at an exchange, the "pink" copy of the Advice Note arrived by post from the Area Sales office on to the exchange doormat. But would the form suffice for digital technology ? And what action would the Technical Officer take? Just listing the functions to be amended comprised a TI of 17 A4 pages. The job seemed endless, and for my staff and me there were simply not enough hours in the day. So I had to take the old and part-finished Instructions on to the overcrowded commuter train, morning and evening, and worked there. Much of the work was "cut and paste", and, at last, I had found a way to keep the dozens of standing passengers at bay, when they spotted the scissors and glue in use. My attempts to dictate into a tape recorder on the train or in a car proved futile. The typists complained of the background noise.

Secondly, I found myself chairing a succession of System X meetings with the Development Engineers on complicated fault analyses for System X, back in the days of rapid transition of on-line data processing from mainframes to microcomputers. This committee was the ultimate in parallel developing techniques, and often the engineers were about to give up due to the sheer complexity of the tasks. My role as chairman was to keep them at it, no matter what, so I gave them as their motto the old Somerset saying "Do summat. Do good if you can, but do summat". This always worked, and I even persuaded them not to attempt to pass fault data automatically from the System X exchange to the fault analysis computer at the outset, but to open Woodbridge with a hand-written fault docket for use as a Batch Input to the analysis computer. Reluctantly they agreed to this as an expedient for the first 6 months. It was used in earnest for 6 years. This study led to a re-think on all the high-tech fault reporting and analysis procedures, and my Group was central in doing both research and development of Area Repair Centres (ARCs) and their microcomputer systems, data from which was "downloaded" on-line to the Harmondsworth mainframe every Friday evening, and batch-analysed.

However, when I arrived in the Commercial Department as Head of Section, it was like stepping into another world. By contrast with all the intense System X development, I stepped back in time, with Strowger extensions, new TXE and TXK analogue exchanges being ordered and installed, and only the first flicker of a System X commercial programme after Woodbridge. This was 1982, and "the show had to go on". Nobody, it seemed, apart from me and my Section, cared at all about Strowger, yet over 90% of the network was working on that system. We were spending £1/3 billion a year on the routine purchases of the Strowger system, and on a flourishing programme of the intermediate-technology TXE and TXK systems. Expensive cost investigations into the final reckoning of the Strowger units occupied about half my staff's time, and the commercial pundits in Headquarters were getting fed up with the gross delays in the mainstream System X, telling me to place a contract to bring in Call Logging on the analogue systems. STC was quick to see this, and improved its TXE4 system into TXE4A, as a worthy and money-spinning stop-gap in the delay period. STC's part in System X development was mainly in the Operations & Maintenance Centre (OMC), a grand computerised office remotely controlling all the day-to-day operations for a group of 60 System X exchanges (of which we had only 1 working at that stage). So at the end of 1982, it came as no real surprise to me when the BT Board announced that they were reducing to 2 the System X joint venture partners, the unlucky party being STC. In 1983, many more System X exchanges were due to open, but were horribly late. Several TXE 4As filled the gap, and the prestige of System X was severely dented.

When the System X programme really did get under way, a new feature came into its own, the Remote Concentrator Unit (RCU), a sort of offspring of a centrally-positioned System X Processor exchange, which was equipped with enough call processing power to cope with the RCU calls as well. Of course, the catch was that 2 complete Pulse Code Modulation (PCM) systems were needed between each RCU and the Processor, but it still costed in in most cases, the only marginal ones being very remote RCUs in Scotland, etc., and such locations where the provision of new cable for the PCM links was expensive.

The Scottish Region realised how marginal some of their costings were, and led a breakaway movement to develop and implement small rural digital exchanges called UXD5s, which could be connected directly into the analogue network without the costs of the PCM links. Naturally, Headquarters, still hell-bent on System X development, gave UXD5 a lukewarm reception, but the first UXD5 to come into service at Glenkindie, Aberdeenshire, in 1979, was the first digital exchange to come into service in the UK, beating Woodbridge to it by 2 years. The UXD5 was a modified version of the BT Monarch private branch digital exchange which, due to its simpler technology, was in full production in both GEC and Plessey. First a 300-line, then a 600-line UXD5 were developed, and my Section purchased over 300 of them for Scotland, North Wales and some remote parts of England, eclipsing the run-up of System X by years. The success of the UXD5 led to sales of several hundred to Kenya. I took part in optimistic talks with GEC, Plessey, and the BT Intellectual Property Unit on "splitting up the World market" and the amount of BT's royalties, but the programme ran out of steam due to the continued lack of support by the Headquarters' engineers, who insisted on System X being driven through, so endangering the UK support base for export sales of UXD5.

Gradually, the Strowger, TXE and TXK programmes diminished, as System X at last came into its own. Newly liberated from most of the former Government shackles, I was asked to operate a new Digital Exchange system contract with L.M. Ericsson of Sweden for their AXE10 system, which was technically the nearest external system to simulate System X's Time-Space-Time mode.

With analogue sales diminishing, and now with a third party making inroads into the market, the pressure was really on GEC and Plessey, who joined forces to form GEC Plessey Telecommunications Ltd (GPT) to slim themselves to compete. Banner headlines on Merseyside read "BT Causes Massive Redundancies". There were strikes, but all to no avail. GPT were now out of analogue production altogether, and my Section had to fish around for small manufacturers such as General Relays Ltd of Crewe and Chester to keep us supplied with Strowger parts for the remaining exchanges. When their Managing Director, towards the end, sought more orders from me, I advised him to diversify into other technologies, but it was too late, and they folded too.

But the really significant point is the drastic reduction in BT's own staffing as a result of digitisation, which is being put into practice as I write. Telephone exchange work will never be the same again, but the additional facilities for the telephone and data customers are great indeed, with even more good things in the offing when the whole network is digitised allowing universal Voice Frequency Dialling.

Just a couple of anecdotes come to mind from all this heady stuff.

The UXD5 contracts were placed non-competitively with GEC and Plessey, on an "equal numbers" basis. Price included Delivery. When the programme came to fruition, it was GEC's lot to make and install the 300-line UXD5 for Fair Isle, a remote island lying between Orkney and Shetland. My old friend and "adversary", Rex Wickham, telephoned to cry on my shoulder, saying that GEC would make a loss on that job, as the shipment from Aberdeen exceeded the average of his unit transport costs by several £thousands. If I had succumbed the whole contract for both GEC and Plessey could have been wrecked, so, using the weight of my Head of Division, I got Rex to wait until the programme had finished, and thus to deal with this one-off extra charge amongst the swings and roundabouts of the whole programme.

The other story is not about digital systems at all, but the TXE4A programme with STC, which that company improved and improved in a bid to step into the System X delay gap. One excellent technique was to assemble huge blocks of equipment in STC's factory to enable better-than-usual testing to occur before issue. This MITRE programme, as it was called, was akin to having a baby in hospital, with all the high-tech testing and remedial equipment on hand. Its only snag was the enormous hole which had to be made in the side of the exchange wall, often at high level, and the large crane needed to lift it in. STC developed special air bags so that, once in the building, several tonnes of equipment could be positioned with fingertip control. STC paid for the building work as part of the deal, but at Taunton Vale removal of the wall revealed that a large structural beam had to be removed and replaced, costing an extra £20,000. I met STC in their New Southgate office and refused to discuss the ongoing national programme until they had paid for the extra costs at Taunton. After hours of waiting I left New Southgate clutching their cheque for £20,000, the only time in 8 years of dealing with the Contractors that I actually received a cheque from any of them, although numerous Credit Notes were generated. Ironically, on the day I retired, a cheque for £13,000 from an anonymous account arrived in my in-tray without any prompting, and was banked by BT under "Miscellaneous".

*Flotation Day of British Telecommunications plc on the London Stock Market. November 1984*

# Chapter 11

# *Privatisation*

On 1 April 1984, the nationalised industry British Telecommunications was incorporated as a public limited company (plc), with the Royal Assent on 12 April and the consequent Act of Parliament to privatise the business. The business of the old nationalised industry was transferred to the new Company on 6 August 1984.

Subsequently, in November 1984, 50.2% of the new Company was offered for sale to the public and the employees, and thus for the first time in the UK, a public utility was floated on the Stock Markets of the World.

This put BT into a position of competition for customer services, and in readiness for this Mercury Communications Ltd, a wholly-owned subsidiary of Cable & Wireless, had been licensed by the Government in 1982.

The 1984 Act abolished BT's monopoly of telecommunications equipment and services sales in the UK, and obliges the Company, through the terms of the Licence under which it operates, to retain many of its old loss-making activities such as the provision and maintenance of public call offices, emergency services and rural telephone service — indeed, service wherever it is reasonably demanded in the UK, with the exception of Hull. On the other hand, the competitors had the choice to market their goods and services where they wished, and naturally went for the centres of the larger cities first. The BT Licence also related many BT price increases to a percentage below the annual Retail Price Index increases, starting at 3% below.

The Government's Office of Telecommunications (OFTEL) issued the Licence, while the British Approvals Board for Telecommunications (BABT) became the national technical arbiter.

BT, however, still "owned" the Network - the infrastructure of local, trunk, junction and private lines necessary to facilitate the connection of calls, which, although by far the business's greatest material asset, is the part which goes largely unnoticed by, and is taken for granted by, the customers and the politicians alike. Under the BT Licence, BT was obliged, if asked, to rent or lease to its competitors lines between nominated locations, to enable the competitors to expand the line capacity by "multiplexing", thus adding value and creating a Value Added Network (VANS). This concept is very similar to the idea that future privatised segments of British Rail, and their competitors, can each run trains over British Rail's track for a hiring fee.

Another feature of the new set-up was the need to enable non-BT customer equipment to be fitted, in customers' premises, to BT local or private lines. This was facilitated by a massive programme of the introduction of plugs and sockets at each telephone point. That enabled the customers to buy their own telephones from retail outlets, and install them themselves. This has now turned into a major part of the industry, greatly reducing the need for a Fitter or Installer to visit after the first connection.

In the period before, during and after Privatisation Vesting Day, I was running the Purchasing Section managing the national contracts for telephone exchange equipment. As this was an ongoing major programme related to long-term contracts, the only real change noticed from a practical point of view in my part of BT Headquarters was the offer of Shares for sale to the employees, some free, and some at discounted prices. Later, profit-based bonuses were paid in the form of Shares. Thus, the implications of the Licence conditions, and the revolution going on in Customer Services were remote from my Section, and I had to keep the staff up to date with the latest developments, in addition to the circulating literature, by whichever means I could. On one occasion around Vesting Day, Professor Bryan Carsberg, the newly-appointed head of the Office of Telecommunications (OFTEL), gave a lecture on the BT Licence to the Institution of Electrical Engineers (IEE) at their headquarters at Savoy Place. After the lecture, I was privileged to speak personally with Prof. Carsberg, and put to him the point that he, as the Government representative in the Industry, had a vested interest in the success of the newly-floated BT plc, but had to make sure that the smaller new competitor companies had a chance to compete — an apparent paradox. The reply was that OFTEL was set up "to ensure that the new private BT succeeds — but not too well !" Thus, the new BT has, since flotation, had to tread a fine line between competition in the market place and withstanding additional regulatory pressures exerted by OFTEL from time to time.

One of the first things to affect BT in its first year of private operation was considerable stringency in its internal budgeting. This, surely, is a moment when the Accountants can justifiably "rule", since a new Company is judged by its first Balance Sheet.

The first results were, indeed, good, but there followed a reactive response from public call office users, which led to a national campaign, with emphasis in London, to raise this specialised service to unprecedented heights of efficiency, despite the call offices being prime targets for vandals. This was achieved with considerable efficiency, and set the scene for the balanced Service vs. Profit profile which has characterised the Company ever since.

The new trading conditions in the competitive market brought on Cordless Telephone developments, and the introduction and expansion of the Cellnet mobile radio telephone network. Then followed an explosion in Customer Data services and equipment, with BT's Research Laboratories at Martlesham now switching its major efforts into the profitable field of Customer Apparatus and Services.

The total digitisation of the switching network has not hit its national target of

1992, and the competing companies must therefore await the total penetration of Star Services and Touch-Tone Keying to enable them to address the customer equipment market fully. London, however, did hit the all-digital target, but cannot enjoy all the benefits in isolation.

While BT plc was being restrained more and more by OFTEL, the competing companies were still to come of age, and technically all was not honey for them. Mercury offered a cheaper-than-BT telephone service to the USA, using VANS, but many businessmen in Britain kept a BT option, accessed via a switch, because in the early days the Mercury version was far from reliable. The arrival of a long row of Mercury call offices at Waterloo Station was much-heralded in the press, but none of them worked when they were brought into public use, before the gaze of the assembled pressmen, who were quick to note the drift of the customers across to the BT row of kiosks which, though a little more expensive, actually worked. My impression was that Mercury and the rest who had now come on to the scene, still had much to learn, not unlike the small private companies licenced to practise in telecommunications services in the late 1800s.

Throughout the first 5 years since Privatisation, BT's share price rose gradually from its opening price, with short-term fluctuations from time to time, mainly reflecting trends and influences in the market at large.

The radical changes which occurred in BT as a result of the different trading circumstances brought on by the new Licences to BT and its competitors did much good to the business in the first 5 years of operation, and, very importantly, have heightened awareness of the importance of Telecommunications in the UK in the Business and Residential sectors alike. The changes also spawned a plethora of organisational shake-ups throughout the Company, which has changed its shape almost by organic evolution.

At the same time, the BT Board, now the Board of a private company, acquired a number of subsidiary companies, some from within, such as Fulcrum Ltd, the former BT Factories Division, and some from outside, such as Mitel Ltd (oddly formed in Canada some years ago as Mike & Terry's Lawnmowers; Mike & Terry diversified into telecommunications equipment, with great success). As with all large company groups, some subsidiaries have succeeded better than others, and the list often changes.

The conditions of service for BT staff have changed since Privatisation, with a steady move towards Personal Contracts, so removing individuals' conditions even farther away from the old Civil Service Pay and Grading, which allowed only limited scope for merit-related rewards and motivation.

During 1988 and 1989, many of the older staff retired from the business, making the new Company a vibrant, young organisation to move confidently into the 21st century. The New Look to the company was typified by the television advertising campaign to stimulate calls through the brilliant acting of Miss Maureen Lipman. This campaign was necessary because, partly due to the tariffing system practised in the organisation for many years, and stoutly defended by the customer pressure groups such as the Post Office Users'

National Council (POUNC), many customers still use their telephones mainly as an ornament, and receive, rather than make, calls. In many other countries, an assumed number of originating local calls are included in the basic charge. This allows retail shops to invite customers to use their shop phones, and encourages them to continue the practice when they get home. The exchanges are kept very busy all the time under that system.

As a tail-piece to my Privatisation experiences, I quote a small ad published a few days after Privatisation Vesting Day in the Situations Vacant column of the London Evening Standard, as follows. "PBX Operator required. Post Office trained. All new BT equipment". Ah, well ! The education of the public must go on!

*Engineering Apprentices at work in the Cambridge Telephone Area, 1960*

# Chapter 12

# *Training and Personal Development*

Training and personal development have always been my first love in my telecommunications career context. My own recruitment and promotion processes always fascinated me, and whenever I met or worked with anyone else I was always subconsciously assessing them and thinking of ways to make them more effective in their work.

My formal stint on Training was at Cambridge from 1958 to 1968. In those days up to about 15 years in a Level 1 post was the order of the day, but after 10 or 11 years there was great danger of getting into a rut, and one had to move on to capitalise on one's good earlier start. I never again found a formal slot in a Training hierarchy, but continued with much of the essence of the work as an extra-mural activity.

For most of my period as Training Officer I was responsible for 150 16-18 year old Apprentices, that is, three yearly intakes of 50. This was the post-war peak boom time, and these lads were the life-blood of the service in the Cambridge Area. In many cases they were destined for higher places as their careers developed.

My personal strategies largely formed improvements on my own circumstances and observations at the same stage. I have already mentioned reporting for duty on my first day in a smart suit. That morning "Titch" Hamilton's gang had to work on an industrial site on the old wartime airfield at Boxted. A new manufacturing company was being connected to the telephone network by overhead wires and, keen to learn, I watched every step. "Boy !" said Titch, "You can make the tea !" On the lorry there was a brazier called a Fire Pot, made from an old dustbin with holes. I chopped and ignited pieces of old pole wood in it, and positioned the vast, soot-encrusted kettle of water on it to boil, and continued my observation of the work. I stood back a little to get a better view, walked backwards into the Fire Pot, tipped over the simmering kettle which put the fire out, and got soot all over my suit for good measure. Titch said "You're no good to me, boy. You can go and help Claud Barber run jumpers (flexible connecting wires) for the rest of the day". I found Claud a pleasant man, and not at all a punishment, but my reception from my mother at home that evening, on seeing the soot on my suit, cannot be repeated here.

On becoming Training Officer myself, I determined never to make any of my lads suffer a first day like that, and spent each first day with them as groups, explaining the job and what they had to do. During this session I issued them with Tools and gave them a pep talk about Accidents on and off duty. Not one of them had an accident on duty, but through the whole of my 11 years about 6 per year had serious motor cycle accidents, including 2 fatal ones from amongst the 500 boys trained. Although destined for technical indoor work, each trainee had to get an appreciation of the whole job, so outdoor Overhead Construction was obligatory. Even those with vertigo (a surprisingly high proportion) had to learn to climb and work on poles, if for no other reason than they had to climb poles on their first Apprentice Training Course at the Bletchley Regional Training School, and would fail the course if they could not climb. Occasionally gang foremen would telephone me to say that a new Apprentice had "frozen" with fear at the top of a pole, and had to be carried down by one of the men. I developed a solution for such cases. At Saffron Walden, 15 miles from Cambridge, there is a large church with a battlement tower. I got to know the vicar, and took each lad with vertigo up the winding staircase to the battlements in the 3-foot thick walls. They always felt safe there because the walls were so massive. The people below looked like ants, and I pointed out a 20-foot light telephone pole beside the churchyard wall, looking like a matchstick. That, I said, was the pole we were going to climb. I put the ladder against the pole, lashed it, and stood out on the wall, inviting the trainee to join me. So far so good. The next stage was to reach the pole steps near the top, and in every case the young men expressed fear about the safety of the steps, so I stood on them myself, and jumped on them with all the force of my 16 stone. By mid-afternoon I had the boys leaning back in their safety belts, re-tensioning the 4 spare wires on the pole. The "advanced" course was to cross the churchyard to the 65-foot stout pole with steps down to the ground. I said I would pass them if they reached halfway up. That spurred them all, without exception, to the top.

I also got groups of second-year Apprentices to build their own small working Strowger model exchange, with the aid of wiring diagrams and recovered equipment, and to accompany me to Careers Conventions.

These boys, when working with the Technical Officers and Technicians, were spread across the length and breadth of the huge Cambridge Area, and I could normally reckon on any two of them at any moment doing what they should not be doing. Keeping the "finger on the pulse" was quite a fine art, as was identifying their particular strengths and weaknesses, so grooming them in the second half of their training to fit precisely into the staffing needs profile I had agreed with the Area Engineer and Executive Engineers.

I also had to organise their Technical Education. The choice between the City & Guilds of London Institute Telecom Technicians' Course (which stood head and shoulders above the other CGLI Technicians' courses) and the Ordinary and Higher National Certificate in Electrical Engineering was always difficult, necessitating judgement of each young man's academic potential early on. To ensure that they were well trained I sat on the Engineering Advisory Committees of the main Technical Colleges in the Area. Some Apprentices, once upgraded to Technician, showed particular promise, and entered the Civil

Service Competition for accelerated promotion — the route I took myself 10 or so years before. I remember entering the inner sanctum in Whitehall for the interview, to find "One of Her Majesty's Civil Service Commissioners" in the chair. "And what do you do when not passing examinations, Mr. Morris ?" "I seem to be failing them, Sir". "Ah, yes. Our mistakes are made to learn by, are they not ? And when was your Royal Grammar School at Colchester founded ?" "It was founded by King Henry VIII, Sir". "Ah, yes; at the dissolution of the Monasteries, no doubt". All this lulled me into a semi-doze, before I was hit between the eyes by sudden questions from another Board member on the electrification of the railway from Colchester to Clacton-on-Sea. I was lucky enough to pass not only that interview but also the whole Competition, in common with just 3 others out of the 400 entrants. Having passed in every subject, the marks were aggregated and an overall passmark imposed. Then the interview mark was added in, and another aggregation brought about the pass list. Most people who were brilliant at Engineering failed English, and it has been my sad experience that most good Engineers find the study of their mother tongue boring, so letting themselves down when writing instructions and reports. While performing moderately well in the Engineering subjects, I was fortunate enough to come top in English, which is probably one reason why I am writing this book, and certainly sealed my fate as a future Head of an Engineering Contracts Section.

These experiences stayed in my memory and I subsequently held, solo or with others, over 1,500 interviews for employment, from Apprentices to Level 3 managers. The key to success in this work, as in most things, I found to be prior study of the job specifications and the candidate's CV, so making each interview unique but fair, against common criteria. I was often disappointed by the lack of flexibility of mind (an essential for Engineering and Contracts work alike) on the part of some second degree holders who had been in the academic world too long, and so were rejected. I never did find the ideal degree discipline for Contract Administration work. The odd Maths graduate was a must, and the occasional Modern Languages and English person, but otherwise I recruited several Historians, Business Studies people, Geographers, Computing Scientists, and even a Theologian. The one Physicist I took on, predictably, joined the Engineers after 6 months on Contracts.

Formal training provided by BT and, earlier, the POED and PO Telecoms, was and is excellent. Personally I always remembered my taught material when putting it into practice. Early on I was given Apprentice training at a POED school in Cambridge, and then at an excellent establishment at Hurley, Berkshire, where Apprentices attended an 8-week residential Course. These schools were combined when the POED took over the old MI5 headquarters at Bletchley Park in Buckinghamshire. Adult vocational training courses were held at Bletchley and the other Regional schools throughout the UK, but the courses involving higher technology such as the range of System X courses and Local Line Planning were held at the BT Technical Training College at Stone, Staffs. This College is well known all over the World, as foreign administrations send their staff there for training. My most daunting experience there was presenting my IPOEE paper on Training to the trainers.

The POED set up an Engineering Management College at Cooden near Bexhill. I attended General Management courses there, and the subject of Safety at Work arose. One accident on duty was shown on the statistics for the Bexhill College, so I asked what it was. Apparently, one Area had sent a manager in his late 50s for refresher training and, being a residential school, he fell out of bed. However, nobody else fell out, so bed boards were not provided.

Then Management Training moved to a former manor house at Little Horwood, Buckinghamshire, with the same high standards. Level 4 managers and above were sent to Henley, Ashridge or Cranfield, where contact with senior managers from other organisations was an important feature. I was always impressed by the way the Post Office and BT standards and achievement stood up well in comparison with people's performances from other companies and organisations.

The evolution of Sandwich Degree Courses at Universities and Polytechnics was a good move forward in the field of vocational training. Not only did it give the employer and potential graduate a chance to become acquainted with each other, it also dispelled any shocks or surprises on the part of both parties and gave focus to the remaining academic studies. Employers could also set and assess Final Year project studies for the students, so enhancing the relationship still further, on a similar basis to re-visiting Apprentices' old schools to demonstrate working models. It fell to my lot each year I worked in Headquarters to interview all the Sandwich Course students in Computing Sciences for acceptance, rejection and placement for 6 months Work Experience in BT Headquarters Departments. On one occasion a candidate walked in, full of self-composure and physically built in such a way that she could easily have competed for Miss World. Her clothes matched that image. Remembering to be absolutely objective, I soon found that she was also technically brilliant, with good flexibility of mind and initiative. I took her on for an important new software development on Area Repair Centres, but on the first day of work, where had our goddess gone? She rolled up for work from her digs at Shepherds Bush on a moped, wearing old worn jeans, a pop-inscription tee shirt and a will to work with gusto which left my staff of Engineers breathless. We soon gathered that she had a different tee shirt for every day of the year. Then, eventually, came the day of presentation of her results to the Head of our sponsoring Division, a man of few words or smiles. The hour arrived but where was the ebullient Effy ? My colleague Peter McKenzie did the presentation for her. Halfway through the lady arrived with weeping cuts, bruises, torn clothes and hair hanging over her face, having been knocked off her moped on the Chiswick roundabout. She and we lived this down and 3 months later we had to present the same scheme to Peter Benton, the BT Managing Director. Again Effy did not arrive, and again she came in halfway through, dripping blood. She made an excellent job of the project but did not eventually join BT, no doubt because she thought the job too dangerous!

I cannot leave the subject of Training without paying tribute to my old friend and colleague Ray Parker. While I was Training Officer, graded Level 1, I was given the responsibility of organising the training of Ray Parker, a management trainee from Bedford, graded Level 2, one rank higher than me. Ray was so thorough with his questions and so searching in his studies of the Cambridge Area that I felt quite relieved when he finished with us and moved elsewhere. A few years later, as a Level 2 myself in the Regional office, Ray was appointed General Manager of the Bedford Area, and I played "Budget cat-and-mouse" with him and his managers. Again, we both moved on and the next thing I knew was that Ray had been appointed Head of BT Training at Headquarters. I had need to contact him from time to time in that capacity, and was very pleased to invite Ray to address the British Institute of Management (BIM) at Chelmsford where I was BIM Branch Chairman. I was very pleased and proud to have kept up Ray's acquaintance since those searching early days at Cambridge.

# Chapter 13

# *British Telecom Overseas*

BT and its immediate predecessors have had a steadily increasing influence outside the UK. However, before World War 2 there was a distinct mistrust of anything or anyone non-British, leading to lengthy delays when brilliant new ideas from outside our shores were either ignored or reluctantly researched. This had to change, however, by the very nature of the substance of the business, Communication. As communication became commercially viable over longer and longer distances, so the field of influence of the POED necessarily widened.

The UK public sector, and especially the Civil Service, was generally introspective from a national point of view, and the purchase, say, of telephone exchange equipment from a non-UK source was forbidden. The manufacturers thus knew that they were feather-bedded and most of the equipment, valued at many £millions per year, was bought at home non-competitively. The POED commercial managers were frequently involved in long wrangles over slight inequalities of allocation of Strowger equipment contracts between the main suppliers. When the System X joint venture, bridging the 1970s and 1980s, also started along the same lines, enough was enough. Looking ahead to the degree of release from controls when privatised, BT at last put the home manufacturers into partial competition by placing a contract for AXE10 digital switching equipment with L.M. Ericsson of Stockholm, through its British subsidiary Thorn Ericsson Ltd.

The strategy for this contract was worked out by the Directors concerned at the Strand Palace, London, in 1985. I and my Section had to finalise the detail of the Contract and operate it. I remember the historic occasion when the first delegation of Swedish engineers and managers visited BT Headquarters. They and we were taken to lunch in our Director's dining room, where (horror of horrors) Diced Swede was on the menu. Fortunately there was no international incident, as their limited command of English made the whole menu an unknown quantity to them. Later some friendly arguments arose on contract clause interpretation because the Swedish equivalent of the 300,000 words in the Shorter Oxford Dictionary is only 100,000. Soon after, the Ericsson board decided that their company could use only English in all its dealings, internal and external.

It would be asking too much to expect my usual "good weather" luck to hold on all my contract visits to Stockholm. I seemed fated to visit Sweden in the

Winter rather than the Summer, and on several occasions the DC8 SAS aircraft taking me there had to land completely "blind" at Arlanda Airport, with the wingtip lights showing up solid cones of falling snow. Indeed, we often had to "stack" while the snow was removed from the runway since the previous aircraft landed. Later, at the hotel, the two thermometers, one inside the double glazing and one outside, showed +25 degrees C and -25 degrees C respectively. These trips were quite arduous, especially as I was the only BT commercial manager present, although several Engineers attended led by my old friend from National Service days, Roger Pine, and Roy Silverson. The normal sequence of events was to suffer the "normal" indignities of British Rail and the Central Line, like any other morning, doing a full day's work running my Section and then, after an incredibly tightly timed afternoon usually culminating in the Director or his Deputy "wanting a word" (unscheduled) on this or that, scrambling down the Holborn escalators with 10,000 homegoing folk on to the Piccadilly Line to Heathrow. I soon learned to travel as light as possible with my pyjamas and razor interleaved with the contract papers in my briefcase which I carried as hand baggage. Not only did this make life tolerable on the tube, it also cut out the intolerable baggage reclaim delay at Heathrow on the way back. Ericssons usually sent a limousine to Stockholm (Arlanda) Airport, and I normally arrived at the Stockholm Sheraton around 10.00 pm their time. There, fresh and bushy-tailed, was the whole Ericsson Commercial Department, regaling me with gins and tonics (I could not stand their rubbery aperitif called Punch) and hoping that, in my supposed worn-out state I would divulge some vital commercially sensitive fact prior to the next day's meeting. I rather enjoyed the challenge of these hearty cat-and-mouse sessions, and (so far as I know) gave nothing away. It was the same in the formal meeting next day at Ericssons' office at Telefonplan, except that the gins were replaced by an endless supply of over-strong black coffee and ridiculously sticky Swedish (or Danish ?) pastries. Few if any of the Brits smoked, but the Swedish side of the table was soon blue with smoke. The return journeys saw me working on notes and contract amendments all the way back on the plane and tube, while loaded down with heavy items in glass crystal requested by everyone in my office. These always activated the bomb check machines at the airport due to the lead content of the glass.

Earlier I was managing the contracts for the purchase of small digital UXD5 exchanges from GEC and Plessey, and heard from BT Teletrade, who were BT's overseas trading arm, that they wished to trial these exchanges in rural Kenya. This involved tropicalisation of the units concerned. As a result BT sold Kenya several hundred exchanges, through my Section.

Some years earlier, when in the Management Services Department, British Telconsult hired Management Services as their agent to study, with recommendations, all engineering operations in the United Arab Emirates Telephone Corporation. In addition to my normal work I was the "UK home base" of the Project, and became the Information and Stores source for my colleagues working on the Gulf coast, obtaining and sending anything and everything from circuit diagrams for the Speaking Clock to roundwood handles for augers. When items required were on the Owings List we had to buy or make them. Later, after I retired in 1990, I was hired as a consultant in Qatar, on the Gulf coast, by British Telconsult, and knew how my colleagues felt in Abu Dhabi 10 years before, when the absence of something which would be of no consequence in the UK loomed large over the 5,000 miles separation.

In another Management Services project I and two colleagues sent information to the Peruvian telephone service, so we attended a "crash" 6-months part-time course in South American Spanish.

Lastly, I am proud that one of my former Engineering Apprentices at Cambridge rose to the rank of Head of Division in British Telecom International (BTI) Submarine Cable Branch, supplying cables, cable ship time and know-how to telephone administrations around the World. British Telecom thus not only keeps in touch with the other countries of the World, but it plays a major part in the provision and maintenance of the World's networks. Latterly these have included Satellite Communication, with BTI Earth Stations at Goonhilly Downs (Cornwall) and Madley (Hereford & Worcester), which have now replaced the old Radio Stations at such places as Rugby, Ongar and Portishead, where earlier long-wave radio telephone calls were transmitted and received.

I hope the reader will excuse just one more anecdote on overseas dealing. My old friend and "adversary" Eric Stuhldreer telephoned me from STC to say that during a stocktake his staff had "found" 54 Main Distribution Frames, all quite old but unused. The "knock-down price to me" was £30,000. These frames were of no use for digital exchanges, and a quick check showed that no Strowger exchange extensions needed them at that time. However, Teletrade had an analogue re-sale export job pending with Zaire, which could use them. I told Eric I would take them off his hands, subject to inspection, for £15,000 including delivery from where they were at Basildon to Teletrade's holding depot at Bridgwater, Somerset. Reluctantly he agreed, and I sent BT's Quality Assurance inspector to Basildon to inspect them. The inspector said that these as-new frames, constituting 3 x 38-tonne lorry loads, were encased in heavy oak crates, but having broken one open, he found that the bolt holes were of Imperial size, not metric. I phoned Eric Stuhldreer gloomily and told him the holes were Imperial. He came to the conclusion that the hundreds of holes would have to be enlarged by BT, at a price. "£7,500" I said. "Done". It was then that I was phoned by the Strowger exchange duty to say that they did, after all, have limited need for such frames at Birmingham and Leeds, and Teletrade called me to change the delivery address to Liverpool Docks. I asked Eric to deliver to Liverpool Docks with intermediate "drops" at Birmingham and Leeds. That was just too much for Eric, who demanded £3,000 to finance his 3 lorry runs. "£1,500". "Done". So we satisfied the needs of Birmingham, Leeds and Zaire for £9,000 against a quoted price of £30,000, which itself was half-price. This was, of course, a "friendly" diversion for Eric and I, as our normal routine deals went into £millions per annum.

Just one eventuality can, I think, spill over from my career into my retirement work for British Telconsult in Qatar. I was honoured to be a guest of a prominent Sheikh who was the General Manager of the local telephone service at a prestige lunch in the magnificent penthouse restaurant at the Doha Sheraton, with breathtaking views over the Gulf. Also present was a 72-year old Swedish gentleman rejoicing in the name of Hans Andersen, who was employed by the International Telecommunications Union (ITU) to visit telephone administrations around the World. Hans told us that he does so much travelling he always travels with very little luggage, and leaves a suitcase full of personal things at every hotel he visits, in each of many countries. As soon as he arrives the concierge simply produces the Andersen case from behind the Reception desk. However, on one occasion this system literally backfired on him, and on arrival at Beirut he found that the hotel, suitcase and all, had been replaced by a bomb crater. The sweet course at the Doha luncheon was a superb dessert, all custard, nuts and fruit. I complimented the Sheikh on his choice of menu and asked him the name of the dessert. He said it was Omali. I said that the name O'Malley occurs in Ireland, too. "Oh," said the Sheikh, "You have this sweet course in Ireland too ?" I explained that I was referring to people, but was worried later as to whether he now thought the Irish to be cannibalistic.

# Chapter 14

# *The Future*

The historical period covered by this book is 1870 to 1990, a span of 120 years, during which much radical and fundamental change has occurred, promulgated both by technological change and by the Westminster political scene at any given moment.

In defining The Future, I would prefer to take a similar 120-year period from 1990 to 2110, than to predict the immediate fortunes of BT. Oddly, there were several periods in the history of the organisation when it seemed as if the ultimate plateau had been reached, eg, the moment of my recruitment to the POED in 1947, but it is now plain that this moment in time was evolutionary, and time did not stand still — far from it.

Also, the slow "ownership" cycle, from Private to Public to Private, over the 120 years, should be evidence enough that the crystal ball of the future is cloudy indeed. The situation of the 1990s is the converse of the stability of 1947, with much rapid change in the Company. Now private, it is not inconceivable that BT itself might be the subject of an acquisition bid if and when the conditions of the Licence are relaxed. If that happened, what of rural communications, and the other loss-making services ? It would be a pity indeed if Lord Beeching's axe of rural railways in, say, the West of Scotland were followed by an axing or charging out of existence of their lifeline, the telephone service.

I have always been proud of the way in which a telephone number is always quoted in national and local disasters, so taking the telephone service and its unseen infrastructure for granted. Long may this unwitting compliment continue, whatever changes occur.

# Chapter 15

# *The Ones That Got Away*

The reader will have noticed that, throughout this book, I have used anecdotes from my personal experience to typify what it was like to live through each segment of the evolving history of the business. There are, however, several other experiences which, at least to me, are interesting, although not directly applicable to the historical milestones recorded in the earlier chapters. These are the "ones that got away", and are now hauled into the net.

My very first managerial position was at Reading, the result of my success in the Open Competition for Assistant Engineer in the Post Office, 1956. I was appointed into the External Planning Group there, and on my very first day I journeyed the 112 miles from Colchester in an atrocious downpour of rain which did not let up all day. I reported, looking like a drowned rat, to Bob Toomer, the External Planning Executive Engineer, who immediately immersed me in dozens of cable plans and distribution diagrams of the Tilehurst area. I tried not to drip water on the precious papers. When we reached 3.30 pm, I interrupted Bob's initiation to explain that I had nowhere to live that night, so a Technician in the Group was given the task of phoning all the hotels, but all were full. This was because both the Atomic Weapons Research Establishment, Aldermaston, and the Didcot Power Station were in course of being built, and there were building workers, surveyors and architects everywhere. In the end I left the office after dark still with nowhere to live, and found a really run-down pub with the odd room for a couple of nights - a place not even the building labourers would use. During the next few days I sneaked the odd moment from the intense work activity to find myself lodgings in the face of great competition from the building workforce, and eventually succeeded in securing a bed about 2 miles out, immediately opposite the Western Region railway marshalling yards where, all night at 20-minute intervals, some demented shunter propelled separate halves of goods trains together at about 50 mph with the sound of an explosion equal to any of the air raid bombs I had heard during the War.

Another fact which seemed to escape my elders and betters was that the vacancy to which I had been appointed was due to the sudden death of the previous incumbent, which made it difficult to ask for guidance when the threads apparently did not tie together; a sort of jigsaw puzzle and cryptic crossword combined, all the time. And still it rained. And rained. Even to the extent of dripping sooty water through the glass roof of the Planning Group on to the precious plans, the product of a couple of dozen steam locomotives a day passing through Reading General station. Gradually I was introduced to all my seniors. The Telephone Manager greeted me with a cheery "No degree, I notice. You'll never make Level 3 !" The Area Engineer droned on and on about how many "waiters" there were in the Area, and I have to admit that I was much more interested in watching his cigarette ash get longer and longer immediately above his fine yellow waistcoat. Should I warn him or not ? Would it indicate lack of attention ? I chose to ignore it, and so witnessed the final disaster when it fell on to the garment.

A couple of months later, after I had acquired the development responsibility for Ascot as well as Tilehurst, I came again from Colchester on a Tuesday morning, only to find the Planning Group apparently deserted at 8.30 am. Had I come on a Sunday ? Had I overlooked a Bank Holiday ? Then I noticed one of the junior Technicians alone in the far corner of the room. I asked him where everybody was. "You mean you don't know ?" he asked. I certainly did not. "They are all at the Ascot Opening Day". Did the Executive Engineer approve ? "Oh, yes. He's there too". And the Area Engineer ? "Yes, and the Telephone Manager. He gets all the tickets". Did he have the keys to the plan cupboard ? No. The key was at Ascot as well. I asked why the Technician was not at Ascot, and soon learned that he had drawn the short straw and had to answer all the phones.

As I could not get to my plans I decided to do some field surveys. Fortunately my measuring wheel was already in my car, so off I drove — to Ascot. Even when a long way off, I noticed hundreds of cars, some of them Rolls Royces, parked on the verges beside the road. I threaded my way through, and found the spot where I needed to measure the road. As soon as I parked on the verge, a man with a satchel arrived and asked me for £5. His pained expression when I told him that I was there to measure the road is beyond description, and he politely invited me to leave and come back another day after the end of Ascot Week.

At the time of my work at Reading both my parents were ill in separate Essex hospitals, so it was no surprise to find myself working back in East Anglia on compassionate grounds only 9 months after my arrival. I would mention that the Telephone Manager knew more about the Ascot Races than about his staff. I was appointed Level 3 23 years later, and Level 4 3 years after that.

My wet experiences at Reading constituted, it seems, all my wet weather for the rest of my career, because thereafter I had the most amazingly consistent good luck with brilliant weather every time I left the office for work elsewhere. This came into sharp relief when I worked for 2 years on Motor Transport Utilisation at River Plate House, Finsbury Circus, London. I worked closely with Ron Kite, also an Executive Engineer who, like me, travelled the length and breadth of the UK frequently. Whatever the season, Ron always seemed to return complaining of the inconvenience of the inclement weather, but when I went out the sun always shone, even in Northern Scotland in Winter. On one such occasion I arrived for the first time in the Scottish Regional Motor Transport Officer's room, and heard him speaking by phone to the Glasgow Police about a POED employee who had just driven a 1-tonne jointer's van along the fence line through the back gardens of two rows of terraced houses, gathering everyone's washing as he went. Well under the influence of drink, he had been put into Barlinnie Gaol to cool down. I said that the jointers in the South would not do that. "Neither would they here" said my colleague. "This was one of my Vehicle Mechanics".

On the same trip I had to initiate a trial of a Limited Slip Differential in a van at Banchory, to measure improved mountain-climbing performance. I enjoyed taking the painfully slow Glasgow-Aberdeen train up the East Coast, as there was always time to ponder over the Angus steaks served by tartaned waitresses in the buffet car. After the Technical Officer at Banchory had been given his trial instructions, he asked me if I would like to see his "other" activity. Off we went up the mountain, where I was surprised to find his capercaillie farm !

Returning to the end of my Reading era, I soon arrived in the Cambridge Telephone Area, where, as mentioned in an earlier chapter, I was given a mixed load including Area Stores Control and Circuit Provision Control. This late stage in the book would not be complete without a final mention of that great pillar of the POED, the "Rate Book". The real name of this series of mighty tomes was the Vocabulary of Engineering Stores, but only some of these contained the "rates" or notional prices of the items of Engineering Stores. This document was something of a "bible" for the up and coming young Area Stores Control Officer. It was kept up to date by an army of clerks in the Headquarters Stores Dept, but not all of them were as speedy as their peers in producing the amendments. Several cases arose where a 1,000-pair cable appeared to be cheaper than the same length of 500-pair, so leading to some very strange cost comparisons associated with Major Works estimates, and subsequent Departures from Estimate. Then there were the highly embarrassing periods when something vital went on to the "Owings List", ie, you could not get it. One such case arose with the total shortage of Rods, Stay, no 5, which were very small stayrods for use to support poles in rural areas. I received chasing letters from every Field Inspector except one, at Bishops Stortford, so I telephoned him to ask why he did not need more Rods, Stay no 5. "I've plenty already". "Where did you get them ?" "From the Railway." It seems that the then British Railways' gathering point for goods lost on the railway was Bishops Stortford, and our local Inspector found their sales were sometimes of "lost" PO Telecommunications equipment. I was able to "buy" the whole Area's needs at one time, at a rate far lower than the current Rate Book price !

But for sheer excitement, there was little to beat Circuit Provision Control - the same duty that gave me palpitations on the Sandringham Christmas Broadcast. A couple of Christmases later I finished my work on Christmas Eve, tired but happy, got in my car, and drove the 48 miles home to Essex for the family celebrations. On arrival at the house, my mother told me that Frank Fable, the Internal Works Executive Engineer, was on the phone wishing to speak with me. The United States Air Force, Mildenhall, had chosen this moment to request immediate provision of a multi-point private circuit with communication between Mildenhall, Lakenheath, St Mawgan (Cornwall), and an air base in Texas. Back I went to Cambridge, and launched, eventually successfully, into the difficult motivation of everyone around the World to do our customer's bidding. When the circuit was working, at about 2.00 am on Christmas morning, I felt too tired to drive home again, so I went to the house of my landlady, Mrs Baker, in Cambridge. Now Mrs Baker, the elderly relation of an office colleague, lived by herself, and was stone deaf. Being a vulnerable female on her own, she converted her house into a Fort Knox when I was not there to protect her at night, so I could not use my latchkey or, indeed, wake her from the drive outside. I was just about to give up when I noticed that the small vent window in her pantry was open for ventilation, so I put a dustbin under it and squirmed in, headfirst. The window was high in the wall, and, being of ample build, I was very careful to manoeuvre myself so as not to displace the pots of jam and the remains of last weekend's joint. Triumphantly I contorted my body to get my legs in, and sat on a vacant area of the top shelf, which, fortunately, supported my weight. (It was obviously not a modern house). My joy was short-lived. Gradually a wet feeling penetrated the seat of my trousers, and feeling down to the shelf behind me in the total darkness I realised that I had tipped over the cup in which Mrs Baker's teeth had been left to soak overnight. Fortunately no damage was done other than a soaking for me. Now I was in, and there was no way that I could get out again without undoing all Mrs Baker's door bolts, so I crept silently to bed. The most difficult manoeuvre of all, of course, was to confront the lady in the morning without giving her a heart attack. To say the least, she was very surprised, followed by a feeling of sheer terror that her Fort Knox had been penetrated. When I returned after Christmas the pantry was in permanent darkness, with permanent close-boarding screwed over the window.

While still at Cambridge my career took an unexpected turn, and there started a long and very friendly relationship with the people of Northern Ireland. Towards the end of my 11-year stint as Engineering Training Officer, I wrote a paper on Apprentice Training for the Home Counties Regional Training Conference at Drayton Parslow. This seemed to be well received, and I was encouraged to publish my thoughts on the subject to a wider audience, which led to its conversion into a paper for the Institution of PO Electrical Engineers, which I read at 22 Centres, including Belfast. The venue there was Queen's University, and I remember being impressed by the warmth of the welcome I received. However, there was no denying the impact of the "troubles", with the security fence around the central buildings in the city, including the POED headquarters. Each gate was guarded by an armed soldier, and I found a moment at lunchtime to slip out to the Post Office to buy some First Day Cover stamps for my children. The Post Office was next door to a large Woolworths store, and as I returned through the gate I wondered how any of the atrocities we know so well can happen, with such high security everywhere. My reverie was shattered on my return, as the whole place was in a state of panic. I soon discovered why, when it was pointed out to me that I must never again leave the building while still wearing my Visitor's Pass. I could have been mugged for it, and the building blown up. Next day, back in Cambridge, I heard on the BBC news that the Woolworths store had been totally destroyed.

Three years later, in 1971, I took over Mechanical Aids Utilisation in the Regional office. On my first afternoon in that post, two Clerical Assistants, tottering under a load of box files, entered my office, and put them on my desk. I asked why they had brought them, and they told me that these were the Regional records on Pressure Vessel Insurance and Lifting Equipment Testing and Inspection. Never having heard of these subjects I asked my Head of Group, Leo Jones, why I had received them. "They go with the job, old boy" he said. "But I know nothing about these subjects" I protested. "You soon will ! You must report to Rugby Radio Station for a Course next Monday, following which you will be the Regional expert !" Before I knew where I was, I had written another IPOEE paper, this time on Testing and Inspecting Lifting Equipment, and was off on my travels again throughout the UK. Inevitably I touched down at Aldergrove again, to present the subject at Belfast. This was a smaller, more specialised paper, so the staff canteen at the Regional office had been chosen as the venue for this meeting of 20 or so specialist managers and staff. When I arrived I was amazed to see over 100 people there, stretching into the distance. The Chairman told me quietly not to get too worked up over my popularity, because most of the attendees were Marketing and Sales staff whose office was destroyed by a bomb the night before. The canteen was the only place to accommodate them. The miracle was that they seemed to enjoy the lecture, and joined in the question and answer session at the end.

Perhaps the most remarkable Irish contact came in 1980, when I left London for a week to launch a field trial of special attachments to the ladder racks of 7 cwt vans. This trial was due to start at Lancaster, Whitehaven, Penrith, Carlisle, Dumfries and - Belfast. Optimistically I dedicated a week to a Grand Tour of all those places, and threw in Budget Meetings at Manchester and Belfast for good measure. I opted to start the week at Belfast, and took the Shuttle from Heathrow to Aldergrove. The staff at Ballarat St depot were very keen to make the trial succeed, but my session with them took too long, and I left Northern Ireland by ferry to Liverpool before I could hold the Budget meeting. However, the Ballarat St people, not being at all sure of themselves, asked that I returned on the Friday to endorse their actions. This I undertook to do, and re-scheduled the Budget meeting for that day. After the usual choppy night crossing, I just caught the train at Lime St, and the rest of my week went as scheduled, finishing up at Dumfries on the Wednesday evening. (The Dumfries Motor Transport Workshop was the only one I knew in the whole of the UK in which loud Radio 1 listening was not obligatory, as the average age of the staff there was 60). When Thursday dawned I really hated Dr Beeching for axing the direct line from Dumfries to Stranraer (especially with the developing cross-country container traffic from Stranraer to Newcastle upon Tyne), and I faced the prospect of an all-day journey by train via Kilmarnock, which more than doubled the actual distance. My POED rank entitled me to first-class travel, which I gladly accepted, occupying a whole first-class compartment which was turned into my office for the day, to prepare the national Motor Transport Budget figures which were due into the Budget Officer in London the next day. All went well until the train reached Ayr on this pleasant Summer afternoon, where the World, his wife, and innumerable children with sticky ice-creams invaded me and my vital papers. A guard shuffled hastily past, well used to the good folk of Ayr occupying first-class seats with second-class tickets. At the next stop, Maybole, they all trooped off again to enjoy the beach in the Summer sunshine. No sooner had I composed myself again than I arrived at Stranraer, only to find that one of the two ferries had been withdrawn due to engine failure. As I had to be in Belfast at 10.00 am next morning I followed the advice written on a blackboard at the ferry terminal, cancelled my hotel booking and set off for Larne straight away. On arrival, after another predictably choppy crossing, I booked into a hotel in the outskirts of Larne, and left a message at the ferry terminal for my Belfast contact next morning to collect me from the Hotel and not to wait for the boat. Next morning nobody came to take me to Belfast, so I telephoned the ferry terminal and asked if my contact had showed up. "Sure !" said the same ferry terminal man I spoke with the night before. "He's right here with me. Do you want a word with him ?" I asked why my contact had not come to the Hotel to pick me up. "Well you see, the boat is late this morning. Engine trouble I believe". When I spoke with my colleague he was just as surprised as I that the ferry man was waiting until the boat docked to tell him that I was not on it !

But all's well that ends well, and we arrived at Ballarat St with just one minute to spare. The news there was not good. They had made a superb job of fitting the trial equipment, but had fitted it backwards. I had to wait to confirm correctness when the change had been made, making me late for my Budget session at Northern Ireland Headquarters. "You are wasting your time with us. We're not big enough to make enough savings to cover your plane fare" they told me. So I attacked their Replacement Programme proposals in alphabetical order. "Crane, Self-Mobile, 5 Tonne, Quantity 1" I read from the sheet. They asked "How can we want a replacement ? We have no big cranes in the Province". I told them the records cannot lie, and after racking their brains they said "It must be that damned old thing in the corner of the yard at Omagh. Hasn't been used for years." I struck it off, saving an immediate £35,000. The meeting flowed better after that, but I finished too late to incorporate Northern Ireland into the national Budget. It would have to wait until Monday. I had not much time to get to the airport on that Friday evening, but an official car had been ordered for me from an office 200 yards away. When it had accumulated 10 minutes lateness, my colleague phoned the transport control, who told him that the car was on its way. Another 15 minutes passed, effectively ensuring that I had missed my plane, but still no car. Could it have got lost travelling 200 yards? "Never mind" said my colleague, "There are always dozens of taxis on the rank outside". We looked out of the window, and for the first time in living memory there was not a taxi in sight. That left only one choice - the Ulsterbus, an experience I would not have missed for worlds. Having walked half a mile to the bus station, I saw the bus to the Airport, a vehicle of truly ancient vintage, with driver to match, thick lens glasses and all. On the inside of the windscreen no fewer than six stickers, one on top of the other, proclaimed to the driver that he should moderate his speed, as the bus had been fitted with a replacement engine, the top sticker no doubt indicating that the 6th replacement power unit had been installed. Slowly the bus crawled through the outskirts of the city, dropping off shoppers frequently as it wound its weary way up the hill past the Divis Mountain. After what seemed a lifetime we approached the Airport entrance, only to be stopped by a soldier with a menacing-looking automatic rifle who came on to the bus and asked everyone on board for their credentials.

I satisfied him by showing my plane tickets, and then he said to the aged driver "And I'll see your licence, Dad". The old gentleman peered at the military youth through his thick glasses, and without a flicker of a smile said "And you such a noice young feller and a poor memory ! That's eight times today you've asked me for me loicence !"

On the Airport, any thoughts I had about an eventful week being over at last were dashed when, now at 5.00 pm, I was paged on the public address system to come to the telephone. It was the Budget Officer from London asking for the Transport Budget. I told him it would have to wait until Monday, but he would have none of it. Reluctantly I told him that he could have the figures that evening after passing through Heathrow, resigning myself to finishing the Budget in the confined space of the aircraft seat — nowhere nearly as convenient as the first-class railway carriage. My misery was complete when, on arrival at my seat, my briefcase containing my supply of paper was unceremoniously taken from me on security grounds, thrust into a thick plastic bag, and thrown into the hold. I just managed to wrench the national Budget figures from the case as it was taken from me. I asked the Air Stewardess if she had a supply of writing paper. She had not. I looked around as the plane taxied for takeoff, and spotted the plastic-lined sick bag in the seat pocket in front of me. I cut it open, and started writing on the plain paper side. Over Manchester I ran out of space, and asked the young woman beside me if I could have her sick bag, and so completed my national Budget Estimates amounting to £80 millions. I arrived at the Budget Office in Finsbury Circus at 7.15 pm and duly delivered the Budget right on to the Budget Officer's desk. On Monday he placed my figures on the sick bags before the authorising committee. This story has echoed down the annals of the business ever since, and at my retirement ceremony 11 years later, Jack Birks, the Chief Motor Transport Officer, introduced me as "the man who wrote the national Budget Estimates on two aircraft sick bags." A month passed, and by chance I sat next to an old colleague, my namesake John Morris, the Chief Inspector of Drawing Offices, over lunch. He told me of an amazing stroke of good luck he had experienced about a month ago when visiting Northern Ireland. He had not ordered a car to take him to the Airport from the building just round the corner from the one I had visited. A uniformed chauffeur saw John walking down the stairs to the exit and asked if he was Mr Morris. "Well yes" he said, both surprised and impressed that the man had remembered his name. "So you'll be wanting to go to the Airport". So it was a month later that I finally closed the chapter of one of the most eventful weeks of my working life, culminating in my friend John travelling from Belfast to the Airport in my official car.

The subject of Security often, it seems, leads to interesting situations, and not only in Northern Ireland. I mentioned in an earlier Chapter that I carried out field work in preparation for live Outside Broadcasts, of which there were many more in the 1950s and 1960s than take place now in these enlightened days of video recording. At the Cambridge Circuit Provision Control I learned that the United States Air Force commandant at the Sculthorpe base in Norfolk had graciously given permission for the 1959 Miss Anglia beauty contest to take place in the truly superb gymnasium at the base. I drove my Technical Officer

Terry Unwin to Sculthorpe, where we met the local maintenance Technical Officer in his van outside the gate to the base. We entered in convoy, with a cheery wave to the guard on the gate, who saw the local man enter and leave several times every day. Having taken us to the gymnasium, he left us to get on with his job while we got on with our preparatory survey to enable these local belles to be seen on the small screen. When Terry and I reached the gate on our outward journey we were accosted by a rather humourless young American Air Force guard, fully armed, who asked to see our entry permit. We said we were from the POED, but he dismissed that saying first that he knew all the POED staff working at the base, and none of them drove private cars. We were under arrest ! As a complete shot in the dark I said "But we have been talking with your commandant about the Miss Anglia competition". "Oh gee, Sir, I'm real sorry ! I didn't know you were from the BBC !"and he let us go. The odd thing is that of all the people involved in the broadcast, none were from the BBC.

Security gets even stranger when regarded within the confines of the POED. Having written yet another paper for the Institution of PO Electrical Engineers, on Network Maintenance, I was given the ultimate accolade of presenting it to the London Centre. It was an evening meeting at the Fleet telephone exchange building in Farringdon Road. I presented myself, complete with projector slides, at the specified door to the building to find myself confronted by a heftily built security guard. He had been given a complete list of people attending the meeting — complete, that is, except for the Speaker ! "No, Sir, if your name is not on my list you do not get in !" I pleaded with him to telephone the meeting room, but he refused and told me to go away. The scheduled time of the meeting came and went, and at last the Secretary came to the door to ask the guard if he had seen me, when the horrible truth dawned. That rescue was only just in time, as the prospect of violence to eject me was looming large.

Another series of happenings which spring to my mind, having just written about my fond memories of Ireland, took place in my fairly brief time in the Regional Network Co-Ordination Centre at Colchester, a new establishment which I had to set up from scratch with very little to guide me. We set up a dial-in scheme for roadworks contractors operating in the Region to come clean and tell us when they had damaged telephone cables. One day the phone rang and there at the other end was the familiar Irish voice of the roadworks foreman installing new drain gulleys on the A11 road near Cambridge. "We've got your cable, guv'nor" he said, "But I know it's not the coaxial". (Coaxial cables carried many more conversations than ordinary cables, so there was much more loss of revenue if they were severed). The Foreman "knew" that the coaxial was on the other side of the road because he had hit it in the previous week. Of course, we knew that there were coaxial cables on both sides of the road. It was common practice for the drivers of mechanical digging machines in roadworks parties to be sacked on the spot when they damaged telephone cables through negligence or clumsiness. When such damage occurred my staff placed an appropriate magnetic marker on a large map of the Region which formed one wall of the office. On one occasion cable damage occurred on the A11 road just outside Norwich. The next day another similar problem arose a few miles away on the same road at Attleborough, where separate roadworks were in progress.

Quickly, a straight line of cable damage markers built up daily, as the same digger driver was sacked and re-engaged by the next gang. In the end we were able to forecast where he would strike again, and warn our Clerk of Works early.

But the most remarkable cases of damage were those caused by Post Office Telecommunications' own operations. One of the more satisfying aspects of my job was to analyse how, through improvements in our staff's own vigilance and common sense, we could reduce instances of damage to our own plant. Sometimes the underground cabling work was done by contractors, and this was the case when "No Communication" was reported to East Bergholt exchange in Suffolk. What was different about this case was that there was no parallel damage report from the nearby working party. Afterwards we found that the cable gang had tried to push its rods into the duct which already contained the single outlet cable linking East Bergholt with the outside world. When they thought they had discovered a blockage, they pushed harder to try to shift it, but were actually severing the working cable and then ramming it into a hard ball at the far end of the duct. Under their contract Post Office Telecommunications had to dig down to repair any misaligned ducts they found, so the foreman went to the nearby telephone box to report the blockage — and, of course, could not get through due to his own unwitting damage.

Sometimes even intelligent forethought brought about trouble. The Oxford Northern Bypass was being built, and the working parties inevitably arrived to put in a new roundabout at the intersection with the Woodstock Road. At that very point a PO Telecommunications manhole contained all the coaxial cables in and out of Oxford C repeater station, in multiple ducts on one wall of the chamber. The Clerk of Works decided, quite reasonably, to demolish the other walls of the manhole and leave the main one, due to the lesser risk to the wall containing the high circuit value. He and the others went home at the end of the day, but in the night torrential rain struck Oxford, and a river of water streamed down behind and under the unsupported concrete manhole wall. At 4.00 am, the weight of the wall made it collapse into the hole the rain had made, and it fell over, so that every high-capacity cable in and out of the repeater station was either cut or short-circuited. When I arrived for work at Colchester, mayhem had already begun, as the World woke up and tried to communicate. All cable communication between London and Birmingham, London and Manchester, and London and Glasgow was lost; and 33% of the London-New York link and half the London-Bristol routes were down. We estimated that in the coming busy hour the business would be losing £500 a minute in lost call revenue. Administrations like Canada Bell guaranteed to restore service by re-routing in 5 minutes, but they had a Service Protection Network. Although such a network was eventually provided in the UK, it was very prone to being used for expedient solutions other than those for which it was designed, and it had significant gaps. But in the event of the Oxford fault we had nothing laid by, so we had to be inventive. The manhole wall weighed several tonnes and was made of reinforced concrete a foot and a half thick, and in any case the 10,000 circuits affected would take weeks to repair. So, as in Canada, we opted for re-routes. That was not easy, as all our trunk routes were busy ones, so we hunted round for new coaxial systems commissioned but not yet in service, newspaper private radio systems which could be used for other purposes in emergency, and the like. By 10.00am we had re-routed every affected circuit, only 2 hours after the effects began to become really apparent. The problem then was to protect our unorthodox re-routes while the repair was carried out in difficult circumstances, as they were not on permanent records. I was astounded when the Deputy General Manager at Oxford told me his jointers would not be available for some time to do the repair, as he had no terminating traffic in these trunk cables, and so derived no revenue from them directly for the Oxford Area. So much for Profit Centres !

Perhaps I can now switch to a completely different occasion, in the Winter of 1979. As Utilisation representative of the Motor Transport Dept, one of the crosses I had to bear (let alone find time for) was membership of the Austin/Morris Small Commercial Vehicle Planning Committee. The problem was that we were buying Bedford vans exclusively in that range, at a knock-down price. Each time I appeared in the Committee in Birmingham it was like a tape record playing identical statements. "Can you say why the Post Office does not buy our vans ?" "They are too expensive." "But are there no special design features which would persuade you ?" "No." Then, one day the spell was broken, and Austin/Morris worked out that they would do better if they looked at the Post Office Telecommunications usage of small vans themselves, and then evolve a more detailed marketing strategy. I decided that they should come to Reading for this venture, since I had more field trials in progress there than anywhere else, so the Austin/Morris party, headed by Mr Denis Mattocks, their Chief Engineer, could see both present and future usage.

I decided to meet these gentlemen at the Beetle & Wedge Inn at Moulsford, where they were staying, in one of our new fleet Princess vehicles, which came from their own "stable". At breakfast time the snow started (uncharacteristically for my outings !), and it increased as the day wore on. Most of our staff were working on windy street corners, and at one stage I wondered if Mr Mattocks was frozen solid. He was certainly seeing what the vans had to put up with. Whether he learned anything I shall never know. Then it happened. The Beetle & Wedge was about 12 miles from Reading, and only 5 miles into the journey the automatic Princess jumped out of top gear. At once the manufacturing experts with me started theorising why, but soon the vehicle would not stay in any gear and we stopped, in the blizzard with night falling, 6 miles from anywhere, in rural Berkshire. We all slithered about, pushing the car off the road in deep snow, then thumbed a lift back to the Beetle & Wedge. At breakfast next morning I do not know if I or Mr Mattocks was the more embarrassed. I insisted that it was poor PO maintenance which was at the root of the problem, but he insisted that Austin/Morris must be the culprits. In the end I agreed, and a new automatic gear box, free of charge, was provided. The sad part is that we carried on buying Bedfords.

It is appropriate and just that I end this PS of a Chapter with a final word on my old Area Engineer, Clifford Riley. In the late 1950s, Clifford improved his productivity by the acquisition of various mechanical aids and specialised tools. These sometimes went wrong, and he lost efficiency by having to wait for repairs, not to mention having to subscribe to someone else's profit in the process. Then an old farm barn came on the market, and Clifford persuaded the Telephone Manager to buy it out of Area funds. One by one The Barn was equipped with lathes, milling machines, power drills and all the tooling needed to keep the mechanical aids in good trim. The Barn also became the issuing point for such small tools as power saws and hand drills. A small staff of Technicians became highly skilled in these arts, and Clifford's Cambridge Area was, once again, the envy of the country. Until, that is, Mechanical Aids Branch in Headquarters got to hear of it. They ordered the closure of The Barn because it had not been given official sanction, nor had it been included in the Budget. After much fruitless communication, during which the already good Cambridge performance grew better daily, Headquarters took the bull by the horns and fixed a visit by a Mr Fowler, with the intent of closing The Barn down. The late Winter of 1955/56 had been frosty, and had taken its toll of the A604 road on the Gog Magog Hills, a little way out of Cambridge. Mr Fowler ran a magnificent vintage Sunbeam Talbot car, and drove from Wembley in it. On the Gog Magog Hills he struck a pothole hard, and broke his back axle. He walked to the Hill Trees pub and phoned Riley, who sent a van to pick him up. Mr Fowler asked who the Cambridge Sunbeam Talbot agent was, but Clifford said he would do all the necessary arranging. While Clifford showed his visitor all the plans of the Barn over endless cups of coffee in the Telephone Manager's Office, the staff at The Barn were feverishly welding the broken axle with all the skill they could muster. Lunchtime arrived, after which Mr Fowler really insisted that they visit The Barn, still with the firm intention of closing it down, thinking that a Sunbeam Talbot agent was fitting a new axle to his car. When he arrived, he was duly impressed with the efficiency of the place, but protested that it still had not been authorised. It was then that the Workshop Supervisor interrupted to say that "Mr Fowler's car is ready". The Barn survived for many more years, and became the role model for Mechanical Aids Workshops all over the country.

And the best thing about all these stories is that they are absolutely true.

# References and Bibliography

*Events in Telecommunication History*
BT Archives and Historical Information Centre

*One World – The History of British Telecommunications International.*
I.E. Shircore & A. Bailey
1991 British Telecommunications plc

*Person To Person – The International Impact of the Telephone*
Peter Young
1991 Granta Editions

*Memoirs of a Telecommunications Engineer*
W.J. Bray
British Telecommunications Research Dept. 1988

*The Recruitment, Training and Education of Engineering Technician Apprentices*
Institution of PO Electrical Engineers.
R.C. Morris. 1967

*The Measurement and Improvement of Network Performance*
Institution of PO Electrical Engineers
R.C. Morris. 1971

*Mechanised Lifting*
Institution of PO Electrical Engineers
R.C. Morris. 1974

*Engineering Efficiency in the Post Office*
Institution of Electrical Engineers AGM 1976
R.C. Morris

*Use of Vehicles in the Telecommunications Business*
IPOEE Journal UDC 656.1 : 654.01. Vol 72 January 1980
R.C. Morris

*Post Office Telecommunications and its Vehicle Fleet*
Modern Transport magazine. March 1980
R.C. Morris

*CAIRO: Computer Analysis of Incident Recorder Output for TXK4*
IPOEE Journal UDC 621.395.344.6 : 681.31. Vol 74 July 1981
R.C. Morris & J.M. Stewart

# List of illustrations

BT Engineers working on the Processor Test
Unit at Keybridge House Digital Exchange, 1984

Flotation Day of British Telecommunications plc
on the London Stock Market. November 1984

Engineering Apprentices at work in the
Cambridge Telephone Area, 1960

*The illustrations in this book have been reproduced
by courtesy of the BT Archives and Historical
Information Centre; and BT Pictures. The picture
on the back of the book jacket is reproduced by
courtesy of the BT Museum.*

*Jacket design and illustration by Brian Denyer.*